AT
LEAST
WE
WERE
MARRIED

AT LEAST WE WERE MARRIED

TERRY C. THOMAS

ZONDERVAN PUBLISHING HOUSE
OF THE ZONDERVAN CORPORATION
GRAND RAPIDS, MICHIGAN 49506

Second printing July 1970
Third printing October 1970
Fourth printing July 1971
Fifth printing October 1971
Sixth printing March 1972
Seventh printing February 1973
Eighth printing April 1973
Ninth printing July 1973
Tenth printing September 1973
Eleventh printing October 1973
Twelfth printing December 1973
Thirteenth printing January 1974
Fourteenth printing September 1974
Fifteenth printing November 1974

Library of Congress Catalog Card No. 75-106444

Scripture passage from *Good News for Modern Man*
used by permission from American Bible Society,
New York.

Printed in the United States of America

To four wonderful parents
without whose love for us
this story could not be told —
MAMA AND DADDY GROOVER
and
MOTHER AND DAD THOMAS

ACKNOWLEDGMENTS

I wish to give thanks to a few of those who so generously gave their time and effort in helping me prepare this book.

Thanks to Sandi Williams, Theodore Sipe, and Pete Gillquist for their labors in editing the manuscript. Each one's comments and advice on the rough manuscript has contributed to the final draft more than words can express.

Also, Carol Ferguson and Mickey Gehlhaar deserve special thanks for their tireless work in typing and retyping.

Without these people, and others too numerous to mention, this book would not be what it is.

CONTENTS

AT
LEAST
WE
WERE
MARRIED

1 Honeymoon Bound

Nancy and I left our hotel Saturday afternoon feeling relaxed and contented. We had just spent our first night of marriage together and were driving south on our honeymoon.

The sun was dropping over the edge of the world spreading behind a radiant golden sunset. Leaving the luscious area behind, however, darkness was encroaching and rain beginning to fall. We chatted about this and that, stopping for a hamburger in anticipation of a fancy dinner later on, but most of all enjoyed the gratification we felt in the bond of marriage for which we had waited so long.

"Oh, Terry, I just can't believe we're really on our way!" Nancy said as our red VW moved us along. It seemed like we had anticipated this forever.

"Um — I know it, sweetheart — seems almost like a dream."

"Just think, honey," she said as she squeezed my knee, "we never have to say good-bye again."

"I don't have to tell you, sweetheart, but you sure have a way of making your husband feel like a king." Neither of us could hold back a silly grin at the mention of "husband" or "wife."

"I don't know how I'd ever get along without you — say, *Nancy Jane Groover*," I said seriously.

"What?"

"What do you mean, 'What?'" I replied with a stern grin. "You're a Thomas now, remember?" I chuckled. Then she broke into a funny grin, a cute smile, and we laughed together.

We were exotically infatuated. Most of our hours leading up to this day had been taken up with thoughts of each other and the future. Now, alone at last — together — was this real? We almost had to pinch ourselves. Marriage was for the other person, or so it had always seemed.

We had fun reenacting the wedding. Nancy had radiated and glistened so, as she softly, but confidently, gave her vows — they will never leave my ears. "I will love, honor, cherish and obey thee," she spoke. I was so overwhelmed as we stood there before the ministers and guests. I guess I felt an awe and anticipation, yet I was hollow with fright. Just to look at her — more beautiful than I had ever seen — all five-foot-three, adorned in white veil and gown, accented with the pink rose bouquet she held. Then the sparkle from her blue eyes met mine in a piercingly exciting way. We had fallen into oblivion and with full abandonment stared at one another and felt ourselves become one. This had been our wedding! Marriage! No longer for the other person. For us!!

The rain was falling steadily now, but we drove on. Perhaps down the highway it rained harder and was darker, but we could care less.

I had stood there in the church, wearing the black tuxedo handed me, thinking about the chase that was to follow the reception. I was not known for avoiding such deviltry at friends' weddings, and several former grooms were hungry for revenge. I wished I could erase every prank I had pulled and vowed that from then on I would always side with the groom.

Rain began to fall a little harder. It was darker further on, but we did not realize it. Actually, we found ourselves tired — but relieved to have the wedding behind.

"Looking back, though, it's all been worth it — I mean now that it's over," Nancy remarked.

I remember her letter to me eight days earlier when we were 650 miles apart. Sweetly from her heart and so full of life, as she always expressed herself, her letter ran through my mind:

My Darling,   Friday 11:00 P.M.

This is the last letter I will ever write to you — or at least for a long time. Exactly one week from tonight at this time and we will be together — married. We should have gotten away by now.

Will that moment *ever* come? A week goes by fast tho, so it *will* be here quickly. Remember when it was twelve weeks — then six, then two? Now only four more days until I see you. How good that will be. The day you left I knew that two weeks couldn't go by fast enough. I surely have missed you — last night especially. Everything hit me at once, and I was awake until about 2:00. . . .

The hotel for the honeymoon looks *out of this world*. I won't even ask you how all this is possible. You certainly are a neat honeymoon planner — too bad everyone isn't getting a husband like you. *Our* honeymoon would be unique no matter where we went, but this is *far more* than I ever dreamed of.

I'm *glad* you have champagne tastes. That suits me fine.

Good-night for now, my love. Only six more nights and I won't have to say that.

How I thank the Lord for you. I can't believe that you will really be mine. You are the most wonderful person in the whole world. I'm a lucky girl.

> I love you lots and lots.
> Your *own* lover

Thoughts darted through my mind as I sat at the wheel. Nancy had fallen asleep beside me — soundly. The blackest part of the evening — 6:20 P.M. — was about to smother us. Raining hard! Our wheels rolled us on. No cars in sight. Highway: four lane. Median: forty feet. Then . . .

2 Nancy Jane

My mind goes back to my first encounter with Nancy. It was in the summer at Arrowhead Springs in California, where I was on the staff of a national Christian collegiate organization. Looking for a high vantage point from which to take a photo of the place I knocked on her hotel room door. She was one of hundreds of other collegians there for the training sessions.

"Hi! I'm Terry. Do you have a pretty good view from up here?"

"You mean of the lawn and the pool?"

"Yeah!" I said, as I made my way into the room and over to the balcony. I looked through the viewfinder of the camera, sizing up the shot, and all of a sudden a thought hit me: I've never seen this girl — and is she ever sharp!

"Say, what's your name?"

"Nancy," she said with a southern accent.

"Nancy, you must be from the South?"

"I'm from Georgia."

I could not suppress a silly grin nor keep from saying, as I turned and looked straight at her, "A Georgia peach!"

She grinned, too, and our eyes had met. I turned back, set the lens opening, snapped the scene, and began to leave.

"Nancy, I'm glad we met."

"I hope the picture turns out okay!"

"I know it will," I said, as I walked out of the room.

Before she left two weeks later, I saw her occasionally and always said, "Hi, Nancy," but was interested in someone else. Nancy had caught my eye though — well, more than my eye — she had a special quality that drew me.

3 Barefoot in the Sand

One evening that following winter, I stepped off the elevator at UCLA — at another organizational meeting — and there she was!

"I know you," I blurted, "Say your name." I blinked twice, and for an instant neither of us seemed to see anything but the other. Her lovely eyes — she was beautiful. I had completely forgotten her. Who was she? Where was she from? All at once I got clumsily excited.

"Nancy Jane Groover," she replied.

Then recollections came pouring in. Last summer — she was that lovely girl — oh — and that southern accent — yes — "Atlanta." I guess at the time my interest had been directed towards someone else, but not now. Conversation leaped ahead of us.

"Where are you going?"

"Down to my room."

"What room are you in?"

"352."

"352? I'm in 452! Right above you, I'll bet."

"Oh, are you the boys that were making so much noise last night?"

"No, it wasn't us; we were pretty quiet."

"Someone kept being noisy real late."

"We didn't hear them."

It was not what we said, but something else in that brief conversation that led us on.

"I'll walk down to your room with you."

She hardly noticed what I had said, just seemed to think I would do so without invitation.

"When do you have to go back?"

"We'll be flying back to Atlanta tonight."

"Where are you on staff?" she warmly asked.

"I'm in Washington, D.C. — I suppose that's about seven hundred miles from Georgia."

I noticed she had an unusual depth of maturity, and there seemed to be a velvet softness inside her, something quietly but confidently to share if that privileged time presented itself. She was acting like an ideal young woman — but she did not seem to be acting — she seemed real.

"Nancy, I'll be down at Daytona Beach for spring break, you know, when a bunch of us are meeting there?"

"Yes, I was thinking of going myself."

"Oh, that'd be so great. I do hope you come — maybe we'll see each other there."

"I know I'd enjoy that very much."

We said good-bye. For some reason I lay awake that night for several hours, too excited to sleep. Nancy was returning to Atlanta that night to Wesleyan College, I to Washington, D.C., a few days later. I considered inviting her to correspond, but then thought, *"Well, no. But what if I never see her again?"*

For the next ten weeks, Nancy Jane often came to my mind. Frequently I was tempted to try to reach her, but always battled over to a position of just waiting.

The winter finally passed, and I looked to Daytona Beach with anticipation that this lovely new friend might be there. I figured if she did not show up, we would probably never meet again, and I surely did not want that.

I arrived in Daytona early one morning and checked in at the welcoming desk. I ignored the forms to be filled out and quickly moved over to the pre-registration file and nervously thumbed through the girls' names. No "Nancy Groover" appeared. I looked through all of them again. Nothing. This would have been the perfect opportunity to get to know her, I mused.

I headed for my motel, disappointed that the Georgia brunette would not be there. The activities of the week began to find their place, however, and Nancy's name faded a little in my mind. I didn't want it to; I just realized I would probably never see Nancy again.

The six hundred of us stayed in the waterfront hotels, and our activities took us from the Hunger Hanger — a nightspot where we put on performances each evening — to gathering in small core groups in the mornings, and to spreading out on the beaches in the afternoons to meet other vacationing college students.

Three of us men were strolling along the beach in our swim gear one afternoon when we bumped into about ten guys our age sitting in a circle in the sand. We could tell they wanted to get acquainted, so we stopped and chatted a moment and eventually sat down. We found out they attended colleges from as far away as Chicago and New England.

After a while, I asked the men if we could share *our* purpose for coming to Daytona.

"Sure," they echoed.

"One thing we are doing is finding out why guys have come."

"Sex," volunteered one of the fellows.

"To get drunk," came another reply.

"Girls," "sunshine," they continued.

Without indignation, the next question was, "Are you getting what you came for?" Puzzled, they weren't sure what I meant. I added, "Are you finding satisfaction in getting what you came after?"

Quickly, and right to the point, it was almost a unanimous, "No."

I was surprised. It seemed like the guys had arrived in Florida for spring break hoping to find that something missing in life. But the search was for more than just the surface goals they thought they needed; it was trying to fill an emptiness inside. So the anticipated merrymaking only complicated the boredom and monotony they had come to dispel.

I asked the men, "Maybe we can share with you guys why we've come?"

They enthusiastically encouraged us, so we simply explained the message of Christ as we understood it.

What we emphasized the most was how gracious God had been in pouring out for us all the gifts we could ever need or want. The "we" was not just the three of us or the six hundred either; it included every person who had ever been born.

Our biggest need was a sense of fulfillment in life and a clear conscience. We could involve ourselves with any number of projects to find this fulfillment, but the only thing to give lasting satisfaction was a complete union with God. This came through Christ whose death provided a passageway to God by releasing us from our guilt feelings — be they large or petty.

I remember explaining one particular verse from the Bible that amplified this important point. It was John 1:12: "But as many as received him, (that is Jesus Christ), to them gave he the right to become children of God, even to them that believe on his name." (ASV) The verse needed little explanation for the anxious men, only to emphasize that Christ was for anyone who wanted Him; it was just a matter of opening up our lives to Him — relying upon Him — while at the same time knowing He understood us if we had difficulty doing so and would come to our aid and help us.

"Do you think that any of you would be interested in knowing Christ like this?" I found myself asking, and three of the men almost fell over each other trying to be first to raise their hands, forgetting for a moment they weren't back in the college classroom. Then questions began bouncing back, and they were not all skeptical. As the three of us fielded the rebounds, the three men who specifically decided they wanted Christ told us that already, right then on the beach, they had begun trusting Him and had started a life of faith. It was terrifically exciting!

The afternoon was warm — but not hot. The surf was pounding steadily as the tide receded, and the beach was so crowded with people one could hardly walk.

Many were passing by, and I looked up for a moment at those strolling through the sand. For another moment I remembered Nancy. I wondered why she hadn't come. Then, suddenly, I saw a girl — I had seen her before. I blinked, squinted, closed my eyes again, looked up, and there she was. I couldn't believe what I saw. She strolled by only twelve feet away with a couple other girls.

Still in intent discussion with the men, it was impossible to jump up and run over to her. *"Surely, she must be looking for me,"* I thought, but girls being girls, I was to find out quite differently.

About twenty minutes later the men began leaving — at least three of them with new life inside — and I headed back down the beach in search of the lovely brunette. Then I spied her in the distance and bounded up as quickly as I could without being too obvious.

She was talking with someone, sitting in the sand as I stumbled by again, unnoticed by those beautiful, lively eyes.

"Can we get together?" I thought to her.

"Oh, I'd love to!" my mind heard her reply. However, I dared not interrupt her, seated there in the sand with another girl who, perhaps, was searching for God.

Back to Silver Sands across the beach I bounced, as excited as a kitten that she was there. Being so involved in the course of the week, though, it seemed spending much time with this beautiful work of art from Georgia would now be difficult, but I was open for any opportunity.

Then that evening came — three evenings before I was leaving for Washington, D.C. There was a warm breeze blowing in from the sea. I stopped before going into the evening meeting. Who was approaching but that lovely girl from Decatur. I thought she would be as anxious to see me as I her, so I hurriedly ran up to her. But, to my surprise, for a minute she didn't seem to recognize me. I started to mumble something and turned to go inside, assuming she would be behind. Once inside, I turned around, but she was gone.

"Nancy, where are you?" my heart seemed to cry out — but she was nowhere to be seen.

The next day Nancy went unfound. I wondered how I would get to know her. In meetings where she should be present I would casually glance around, but to my disappointment, she was not to be seen. Then, finally, chance opportunity presented itself. I had slipped out of a crowded meeting which was going a little long. Hearing whispering behind me in the lobby, I quietly turned around. There stood Nancy — but with another guy. We said "Hello." Then the fellow stepped back into the meeting, and there we stood — Nancy and I — alone.

"I'm glad you're here, Nancy," I said.

"We almost had to stay at school, but at the last minute we were able to come." Her voice retained that special quality: soft and warm, flavored with her southern accent.

"Remember chatting in front of your room at UCLA?" I smiled.

"Oh, yes," she warmly replied. Her eyes lit up. But an attempt to ruin this opportunity was creeping unawares.

A friend of mine, my superior, Dick Ballew, was arriving in Daytona for the first time that week. Dick and I had not seen each other for over two months, so, naturally, we were anxious to get together. As I had approached the lobby from the inside, Dick approached from the outside, and as Nancy and I began to talk, Dick entered the lobby. I was glad to see him — but not just then.

"Terry, good to see you."

"Dick! Hello, just get in?"

"Yeah — say — I could use some coffee; come on along and we can talk."

"Okay, Dick, sure — uh — good-bye, Nancy."

"Good-bye, Terry." Nancy stood there, alone.

I began wondering if we would ever get together. Nancy had seemed friendly and receptive. I must admit, though, I was not sure what was going through her mind. Then I had a perfect opportunity to find out; it wasn't deceptive — just sneaky.

The next evening, the night before Easter, seated in a meeting in the same auditorium, I spotted Nancy about six rows in front of me to my left. Some guy was sitting next to her, but I did not know if they were together.

Then once or twice I noticed she turned around and looked back over her shoulder. For an instant she looked my way, but her eyes swept the entire auditorium. Had they paused a tiny instant extra on me? I wondered if it was my imagination, so thought I would lay a trap.

A fellow I had met that week, Tommy Ellison, had become a good friend and was sitting beside me. He knew I was interested and kept commenting on how tremendous he thought Nancy was.

During a break in the meeting, I whispered, "Tommy, keep your eyes on Nancy for a few minutes and tell me what she does."

"Okay, Ter — gotcha'!"

Meanwhile, I put my arms on the seat in front and laid my head down. It was but a few seconds until he reported in a whisper that she was glancing back, then, "Ter, she's looking at you!"

"Well, coincidence," I thought. However, if she did want to look my way, she would think she was safe, believing I could not see her. A second time Tommy reported her eyes were sweeping the auditorium. An instant later, the same excited report. "Ter, she's watching you." Tommy was jubilant, and I knew I had won. *"But what should I do now?"* I asked myself.

4 A New Kind of Easter

At six the next morning, I rolled over and looked at my watch. I was singing in the Easter sunrise service choir and was supposed to line up to sing at ten minutes to six. Had it not been that an exciting determination had come to my mind the previous evening, I would have put my head under the pillow and slept on. But I jumped out of bed, piled into my Volkswagen, and tore down the beach. I had a plan, and the only obstruction would be Nancy's not showing up. Stopping the car and jumping out, I ran to where the choir was to meet. Everyone was already assembled, and as I quickly made my way to my place, to my gleeful surprise, the fifth person I had to pass was Nancy Jane.

"Nancy," I blurted out, pulling her aside, "I want to talk to you for a second." She looked up with a puzzled smile. "How're chances of taking you to church this morning?"

"Well . . ."

"Pretty good, aren't they?" I was overconfident.

"Terry, I don't have anything to wear."

"You look great just the way you are!" I didn't notice she was in pedal pushers.

"Well, all right."

Later that morning I was proud as I knocked on her door to pick her up. The red compact was all shined up, and off we scooted. Nancy had found a pretty yellow dress, too.

After church, the foiler's pounce was not far off again, though, for a friend of Nancy's wanted a ride home.

"Will we ever get to be alone?" I thought. However, we dropped off the innocent and appreciative friend, and I suggested we go for a little drive.

"That would be fine," Nancy casually replied. We rambled along, and pulled up about five miles down the beach on a rather secluded clump of sand. A deep affinity developed between us as our conversation continued.

Somehow my palm slipped next to hers and our fingers unconsciously entwined. It felt so good when we noticed what had happened. A little thing, but it was wonderful and our hands seemed to fit together so well.

Two o'clock, then three — neither of us had had dinner, and by now we had missed the meal that was furnished. I imagined dining Nancy in a fine Daytona restaurant, but looked in my pocket to find just one dollar. Luckily, I spotted a fellow back at the Silver Sands who owed me ten dollars, and we pointed the 1300 VW limousine towards Howard Johnson's

We stuffed ourselves with delicious top sirloin, salad, and baked potatoes and chatted our way through about an hour and a half. I had just put my fork down when Nancy innocently asked, "Terry, have you ever been bad — I mean like bad with girls?"

She caught me so by surprise, I almost fell off my chair. I stopped and thought a minute as I looked across the table into her innocent and pretty blue eyes. Then I leaned back, took a sip of coffee, trying to think just how to word it, and began.

"I always thought about God a lot, Nancy, I mean even as a kid. I didn't really know what He was all about, but tried to learn. When I was eleven, we had some special meetings in our church which shook me up quite a bit — I mean, I tried to live a better life after that, but it only lasted a few weeks. I had a few other similar experiences along the way, but the one that really made a lasting difference came when I was nineteen." I took another sip of coffee.

"Spiritually, my life had become a series of frustrated up and down moods, and for some reason when I graduated from high school, I felt if I could live in a Christian atmosphere, the Christian life would rub off — sort of like osmosis — and give me a true inner peace. So I set off to study the Bible at a Bible institute, believing it would be the answer."

Nancy was listening intently. Her nods and facial expressions of curious interest led me on.

"I didn't do too badly there, but as time went on found myself performing and acting, not genuinely being myself. Certain rules and requirements demanded performance, and all the students were rated as such.

"I found outside interests, though, like a good job, going out a lot, fixing up my car, and so on, but for some reason I was definitely missing true, inner contentment.

"I began to lose interest in my studies. Studying the Bible was giving me a lot of facts in my head, but didn't help my life at all, and one Wednesday my roommate and I — we felt about the same — received little notes in our mailboxes asking us to leave school. I reacted with, 'Well, if that's the way they feel about it, fine with me!'"

Nancy chuckled. "I can just see you, Terry. But then what did you do?"

"Well, I still wanted to find the real answer to life — it made me mad that I had tried so hard to find it and couldn't. I knew that *trying* to clean up my life wouldn't work — I'd been that route too many times. I knew that just studying the Bible wouldn't help — I'd done that for a year and a half. If there was an answer, I figured somehow I'd have to work it out on my own.

"Meanwhile, a fellow who seemed to have a unique understanding of us boys had joined the staff that year as the dean of men while studying with us in our classes. Without any pressure to make us perform, Ted seemed to have a way of accepting us just as we were. You know, someone you didn't mind talking to about your problems.

"Ted and I had talked earlier that week about me leaving, and he had hoped to see me before I left — he wanted me to talk to the faculty and stay there at school. 'God is going to use him!' a premonition seemed to say. But, instinctively and rebelliously, I wanted to avoid him. So I determined within myself not to be caught with Ted alone."

"Did you see Ted then?"

"Well, I don't know how it happened, but the Saturday night that I was ready to move, I looked over my shoulder, and no one was around except Ted. 'I'm not going to say much,' I said to myself.

"I remember it vividly. I could take you to the exact spot, Nancy. It was dark and clear, and I gazed up at the stars. Nothing was said for several moments; then, 'Well,' Ted spoke quietly, 'How is everything?'

"'I'm on my way, I guess,' I kind of echoed, determined not to say more. I can't remember what he said next, but within instants I sensed a tremendous spiritual awakening in my life. I can't say theologically what happened, but I know that in that moment I found an inner peace that's never left."

Nancy was following each word carefully.

"I knew that working at the Christian life wasn't the answer. But if Christ wanted me just as I was — I mean, if He would accept me for *me,* and not for what I would *do* — I would more than gladly let Him. And that was the point. For the first time in my life, I gave up trying and let Christ have me. Ted kept talking, but I didn't hear another word. My mind muttered silently a little two-worded prayer, 'Okay, Christ,' and Christ did not take long to prove His power."

Nancy took a deep breath, as though she had just been through it herself.

"I know that Christ takes us each where we are, dealing with us strictly as individuals, and that not everyone will have an experience similar to mine, Nancy, and it is not necessarily better than others."

"You mean that when people open up their lives to Christ, He will always come in, but the emotional responses may vary with each person."

"Yeah. I've since seen men calmly and unemotionally, as though they were just buying a pair of shoes, invite Christ to have their lives. They weren't immediately filled with emotions for Christ; they simply trusted. Through time, though, they have experienced the love and the peace and the joy that only Christ can give — although their immediate experience was different from the kind Christ gave me."

"I sure agree. Then what did you do next?"

"Ted continued talking, and I had to interrupt to stop him. My mind had wandered far away and already had formulated plans. I didn't even stop to tell him what had happened or my scheme; I was so excited. I simply said, 'Ted, I'll be back in an hour.' I jumped into my '49 Chrysler and headed out to see my employer. Arriving at her home, I cruised in with a lighter heart than ever in my life and explained what had happened. I also expressed a desire to cut down on work in order to devote more time to school. I didn't need all the money; it was only selfish ambition that sought gratification in working so heavily. She agreed to rearrange the schedule and do whatever would be best for me."

"That's neat."

"I quickly returned to Ted, who was still waiting, and explained to him all that had transpired, and we rejoiced together. I still had to meet with the faculty later and state my intentions to be reinstated."

"Your life has been a lot like mine, Terry — I mean trying to find Christ in the wrong way for a long time."

"Really? Well, I guess I'm not too surprised — tell me, Nancy."

"Well, the summer before ninth grade — at camp — I first heard that you must ask Jesus to come into your life. Immediately, I realized I had never done this, so I invited Him in as I walked forward. But I soon fell into a trap — that of determining to live a better life. But the harder I tried, the more I failed.

"Then the summer before my sophomore year at Wesleyan, God showed me how to really be free. I learned to trust Him when He said He would live through me, so that walking in the spirit is 'doing what comes naturally.'

"I realized that God must come first — His will must come first, and to find what His will is, we must be willing to know first. What He showed me that really set me free, though, was that He was *all* that I needed — totally all. For the first time I knew that I loved and wanted the Lord desperately, above all else. He, in turn, filled my life Himself, and I knew I could be completely happy because I had Christ, was in His will, and that was all I needed. Thus, I was liberated from worry about my future — who I would marry, etc. — never to be bothered by it again. And I saw how fruitless self-effort is.

"My faith grew through disappointments, and in spite of them I found myself having hope for the future instead of despair and bitterness. He showed me that freedom in Him isn't freedom from responsibility. When I got discouraged and thought I would leave His work to someone else, I found myself in situations where, for the first time in my Christian life, I was able to overlook my own lack of ability and allow *Him* to do the *impossible* through me. I finally quit saying, 'I can't do this, Lord,' and said instead, 'Lord, I'm scared, but I know You can do it.'

"But to get back to you, Terry. Did things start to change all at once, or were the changes gradual?" she asked.

"Well, both," I chuckled. "One that was immediate, I'll always remember. I worked the next day, but the minute I got off work, I could hardly wait to get to my room and read the Bible. I rushed into the room, closed the door, grabbed my Bible off the shelf, and dug into the Book of Romans. I don't know why, but I can see that day like it was only yesterday. I read the book from cover to cover in one sitting, something I had never done before — except, perhaps, the half page book of III John."

Nancy chuckled.

"I don't suppose I understood more than a small part, but what I did understand was very personal. Up to then, Bible study had been something I did only for classes and examinations. I could never concentrate if I wanted to read for pleasure, even though I'd learned a lot of outlines and doctrines from it. I had even memorized scores of verses — some whole chapters and almost a whole book. But it had been of little value in application to my life. For the first time, it became warm; its message was thrilling! And for several months, it was all I wanted to read. I wasn't interested in studying it at all — seeming to be able to grasp and understand all I needed by mere reading.

"And this brings me to the answer to your original question."

"What do you mean?"

"Well, I think the greatest single fact I learned was that Christ had died on the cross to completely forgive me of my sins and shortcomings."

"Yes."

"I had heard the words before, but now it began to be an experience — a warm experience from understanding that God had, out of tremendous love, given His Son — the one whom He cherished and from the depths cared for — that they, He and His Son, might be separated for a time, so that He could pour out all of His anger and wrath upon Him instead of pouring it upon me. I began to see that I had not been measuring up to His standards, that I needed His Son Christ, who *had* measured up, to bridge the separation between us, and that this would work in everyday shortcomings from then on. In other words, every sin I ever had or ever will have, God no longer saw — or sees — and He accepted me just as I was — and I began to, too."

I paused a moment and finished my coffee.

"Well, that's pretty much the whole story. That was just the beginning, you understand — I have had a lot of growing to do and still do — but this is certainly the right track. I know you understand this — it's just a beginning and often I have trying days. It's not been all silk and satin by any means."

"Oh, Terry, that's so neat."

"So, then, what about 'being bad,' or 'sins'?"

"Terry, I don't care what anyone has done; if they have opened themselves up to Christ, He has forgiven; if they haven't received Him yet, He still has forgiven them — they only need to open their lives up to it before it's credited to them."

"Yes, and we can forgive ourselves — and each other."

"Yes!"

"If we haven't truly received Christ, and at the same time have not done anything gross by the world's standards, we'll have a tendency to feel proud. And if we've really goofed it up morally, we'll feel guilty. So really, what we have or haven't done is irrelevant — it's worthless and best forgotten, both the good and the bad. Only to leave it all behind and latch on to Christ."

"Terry, I couldn't agree more," she added, in her calm, feminine way.

We left the restaurant feeling much closer than before.

The day was full of varied experiences, including one with the police over parking in a No Parking zone, and I almost had to go to jail in a squad car. It took us until after midnight to retrieve the lost carriage, for they had towed the VW away, but after nearly eighteen hours together, we had anticipated those last minutes for drawing things to a close.

Early in the day I had confided to Nancy that I was basically through dating and would not ask a young lady out unless I felt that there was a possibility of a future permanent relationship. This completely put her at ease for she then knew exactly where I stood, and we could be our real selves with each other.

It was two in the morning when we pulled up on the beach near our motels. The surf was still quietly and rhythmically thumping the shore, the usual warm breeze was blowing, and the full moon was so clear we could almost reach out and touch it.

With the future ahead and parting only hours away, we took off our shoes and strolled down the beach through the cool sand. I heard myself softly whisper into her ear, "Nancy, we best give our relationship a little time to double-check itself, but I feel confident that you are the one for me."

She seemed to have all the qualities of my highest ideal — and more — and the feelings inside pointed towards love. She felt exactly as I did but was a little more afraid of her feelings and almost could not believe them.

"Why do you feel sure?" she quietly asked.

I reviewed the situation exactly as I saw it. "Maturity, faith, love, not just surface or even deep infatuation, Nancy, a balance of personalities, and just a certain assurance — but we will not rush."

"Terry," she softly replied, "it all seems too wonderful to be true."

We had wandered far down the beach and into the night, not wanting to say good-bye. Deeply in love even at this early stage, we did finally say it, but not with ease. We made our way back to her room. A warm, golden Monday morning was just breaking when I brushed aside her bangs and softly kissed her on the forehead. We said nothing for several moments.

Finally I whispered, "I'll be down to Atlanta to see you soon," and left with the dawn.

5 Send It Airmail!!!

"What a Father we have, and how I long to see Him face to face and feel His warm and comforting arms. That might sound kind of dramatic, but I think about it a lot and just try to imagine what it is going to be like to be with the Lord all of the time in body as well as in spirit," Nancy radiantly said in one of her letters as we began to correspond.

Even though we felt a strong attraction for each other, a question deep inside kept saying, "Will it last?" or "Will it fade away in time?"

So I was anxious to learn Nancy's attitude when letters began arriving. I found myself thoroughly excited, more than ever in my life, and each day eagerly leaped to the mailbox as soon as the mailman's blue cap flashed into sight. It was about a week later, however, after receiving my first letter, that Nancy responded with her second. I ran up from the mailbox, tore into my apartment, flopped into my one easy chair, and quickly opened the envelope, being careful not to tear the contents.

Dear Terry,

I'm afraid this will have to be short since it is late and I am *real, real* sleepy.

I, too, can hardly believe a week ago tonight at this time that *you* were about to get taken to jail and now you're nearly 700 miles away. It's hard to realize, and I, too, will hope that the Lord will bring us together before too long because I am anxious to get to know you a whole lot better. In fact, I find myself thinking about this an awful lot, though I try not to. I'm really having to trust that He will control my thoughts as well as what

I say and do because I have a tendency to try to preplan His plan, as I told you. This is something you can pray about.

I sat back in the chair, took a deep breath, and let the excitement calm down a little. I quickly scanned the page again and felt very encouraged — she had well expressed the tone of our relationship at that time, too.

To add to the excitement, Tommy Ellison wrote:

"We all love you very much and are praying that Nancy is the right one and that God has her in mind." He had a way of seeing in and through people and could tell that Nancy was one of the most ideal girls he had ever known.

Still, that little question down inside kept secretly saying, *"After we're apart for a while, will Nancy lose interest?"*

As letters piled up, Nancy and I could not help getting into the subject that was at the very heartbeat of our lives individually, entwined between us, deepening and enriching our relationship. The subject? We were discovering practical thoughts from the Bible that helped us in our everyday lives. We were not concerned about theory, but about discoveries that translated into everyday experience, benefited in a pragmatic way. It was not something we felt we had to talk about — there was no law or regularity to it — just something that developed and happened on its own.

One such discovery was from James 1:25, "But he who looks into the perfect law, the law of liberty . . ." (rsv) seemed to show us that now as believers we were free to live by trusting Christ without a system of rules. We could do what we really wanted to, and naturally, without pushing, good works would in their time and place result. This discovery was in pleasant contrast to the often felt pressure to perform and produce for God.

Nancy wrote:

It's interesting that you should mention what you did about James 1:25 because I have been thinking about that a lot lately. You are so right — we are *set free,* and sometimes God wants us to do what's hardest for us — slow down.

Your letters draw you so close, but not close enough. Terry, it's really neat the way the Lord is working in this, tho, like you, I have a kind of peace that I've never had before in this type situation. What all this means? I am still trusting the Lord to find out. I feel great tho, and haven't felt so full of His love and everything else in a long time.

Terry, I hate to quit writing this because as I've said before, it draws me so close to you. But it also makes me really miss you. In fact, I wish I could hop on a plane right now. Why don't you just sneak off to Macon for a weekend? (This sure didn't make me feel too bad.)

I'll be thinking about you as I talk with Him in prayer tonight, and I will continue to pray, Terry, that He will use you to your fullest. I hope along with you that He will use you in a tremendous way with lots and lots of people because I know that this is what you desire. Take care and let me hear from you soon and often.

> With all of His love and mine too,
> Nancy

I sensed in myself a desire to proclaim God's good news to folks all over the world, and I began to see how fantastically Nancy could fit in as an ideal complement. A perfect match? It seemed more like it every day.

The speed with which things were happening was sort of a shock, though I was enjoying it thoroughly. I had written, "Nancy, you know how much I think of you, but sometimes I find it best to hold back words — though that isn't always easy."

It was a warm spring afternoon when her reply arrived. I leaped outside, ripped it open, and flopped down on the freshly mowed grass. Before I was through reading, the news had me rolling with glee in the sweet-smelling green clippings:

Dear Terry,

I just have to write to you before I go to bed and tell you how much I've missed you. You know, I've been saying how well the Lord has disciplined my mind lately to keep from thinking about things? Well, He must have decided that it was time for me to become *undisciplined*. At times I can hardly *stand it* and feel like there must be *something* that can be done about it. Terry, this is all just really hitting me hard, and pray that my feelings are *completely* from Him. You see, I am so used to being confused by my own feelings that I don't know whether to interpret them as being from me or the Lord. In fact, I still have this mental block about being so open with someone *so soon*, because it's against everything I've *ever* been taught — you know the old stand-bys, "don't rush into things," "don't wear your heart on

your sleeve," "you shouldn't let him know how you feel so soon,"
etc.

Yet, I know what's in my heart, and I can't hide it or make it
go away, and I just felt like I *had* to tell you.

Terry, my feelings are becoming *so* strong that I pray that He
will lead you even more clearly and strongly than He will me.
I'm going to trust Him, but I'm also trusting Him largely to show
me things *through you*. So I'm really praying that your feelings
are of Him. . . .

I could barely believe my eyes. I rolled over onto my back and
looked up into the blue sky. Relationships I had usually experienced were too often conflicts for leadership. But it was clear from
the Bible that a marriage should have a husband who could and
would fully love and honor his wife, while his wife willingly
and voluntarily submitted to him.

Then I thought ahead a little. Submissiveness does not happen
in a moment at the altar, either, but must grow and be developed.
If we were to have this kind of ideal relationship, it had to begin
now — and here it was.

So three weeks after leaving Daytona I began to think of
scooting down to Atlanta for the next weekend. Knowing that
the 650 miles each way would make a long, tiring trip, I did
not want to go if this were not possibly permanence in the
making.

Then, to complicate matters, a couple of days later I received
a letter from Nancy which could have caused some doubt in the
whole affair. Our emotions had been at such a high peak that
they could not hold forever, and thus, part way down, they
tumbled. It was a healthy reaction, though, for love must go
deeper than just emotions.

If when our emotions lagged, our love lagged too, then it would
not really be genuine love — only infatuation or being in love
with love. I told Nancy about my feelings as emotions subsided
a little, and she openly and warmly confided in return:

You know, there is something quite wonderful and unusual
about the way that our minds seem to run along the same lines.
I couldn't believe what you said about not feeling a "great love"

all the time because that is how I have felt several days now and then.

Before it would have bothered me, but somehow, now it doesn't. Because, tho the emotional feeling isn't real strong, there is a real calmness and contentment. I've done a lot of thinking about this exact thing, Terry, and you know I've come to decide more and more that the way the Lord has love planned is really perfect. I think if we did have this strong emotional feeling *all the time*, it would become too much for us to bear. Our minds and bodies couldn't stand it. I'm sure that married people don't go through every day with this feeling. It is funny because I started to tell you about this earlier but just never did.

Even though our emotions diminished a little, my mind and common sense said to drive down to see her. So I figured that if after three days, I consistently felt impressed in this way, I would call Nancy and make plans for the following weekend.

Three days later I seated myself comfortably in my easy chair, put the phone on my lap, and, with shaking fingers and shortened breath, dialed the Georgia number — and waited.

It was the dorm phone that rang and a girl at the desk answered: "Nancy Jane? Just a minute, please." Then, in that cute, slow southern accent my ear had almost forgotten, "Hello. Oh, I'm so surprised — I'm so glad you called." I shook all through with excitement as our conversation led on and on.

"Terry, how have you been?"

"I've been just fine."

"Seems like forever since we were together in Daytona."

"I know. Nancy, I've had a thought I can't seem to get rid of," I teasingly said.

"Oh, what do you mean?"

"Suppose I could get you home next weekend if I were going to be there?"

"Oh, do come down — that would be just wonderful," she persuaded, and, of course, I knew I would. "Terry, I just can't believe you'll really be here."

"I can't either." We couldn't seem to say good-bye, and it was an hour later when the two receivers did click down, totalling up a Bell Telephone bill higher than the cost of gas to propel my VW the 1300 miles to see her.

Looking ahead to the weekend seemed like forever and a big, beautiful mountain full of delights that would never end. It was impossible to see beyond the mountain, yet, a wild question dashed through my mind! *"Would we find we had made a mistake?"*

In her next letter I thought I sensed a bit of waning in her excitement over our relationship, though it was only my imagination. I knew that she was as assured as ever. I could easily have asked, *"Is this fading?"* but dared not, though in a corner of my deeper heart laid at least a little fear.

6 Georgia Bound

With pounding heart, Friday morning I nosed South. Letters had revealed Nancy's character which matched her beauty and charm: strongly desiring love — able to fully receive it and return it — maturely understanding spiritual truth, feminine, humble, and, above all, submissive. To say the least, I liked her a lot.

After reaching Atlanta, I really blew it. Nancy's exit was on the north end of town. I blindly skimmed past it and wound up in the heavy downtown Atlanta traffic on the busy Friday evening. Finally, on the other end of town, I managed to pull over to a service station, and, being completely lost, made my way to a phone. I fingered through my pocket, found a dime, and dropped it in the slot.

"You're near Playland? An amusement park?"

"Yes, and I'm sure mixed up!"

"I just don't know where you are. Let me ask daddy." A moment later, "I think he better explain it to you. Oh, I'm so glad you are here. I'm just so happy you came."

"Hello, Terry." I sensed a wide smile shining through the warm southern accent. "This is Nancy's father. Now, where did you say you were?"

Somehow, we managed to get it straight, and I streaked my way toward the service station where Nancy was to meet me to guide the way home. I felt sure she would be waiting once I got there.

But at the appointed meeting place I waited and waited and waited. Already a full hour had been wasted getting lost, and my anticipation to see Nancy grew. Maybe that was what she wanted.

The warm spring evening provided an ideal setting as flashes of memories and words from letters moved through my mind. Finally, well beyond my endurance point, she pulled up. By this time, my excitement had passed into numbness.

"Nancy Jane — so this is you." I grinned gigantically as she stepped out of her car. She was everything I remembered.

"Hi, Terry," she warmly, but almost shyly, replied. "Have you been waiting long?"

"For a while."

"Oh, I didn't think you would get here so fast."

Then we didn't know what to say.

A lifetime had passed, it seemed, since I had brushed that kiss on her forehead at Daytona Beach. Now we just sort of stood together — she leaning on her Impala, I on my foreign compact — face to face — holding hands.

Wouldn't we live forever? Could anything ever diminish the feelings that had been aroused for each other? Lack of interest? No! Change of mind? Never! Death? Who ever thought of that?

Our hearts and minds had been drawn so close together through letters, but what a different story to be face to face. The letter is now a warm person, right in front of you, and you realize that though you know the letters, being with the person is something quite different. Then you meet the family!

Although I am a little shy in strange, new situations, I experienced a freedom and ease the moment I stepped in the door. I felt I could just be myself. Mr. and Mrs. Groover were so genuine, so sincere, and so kind and interested in me from the very start, though not forceful or pushy. I knew immediately they were my kind of people.

We had come into the house and seated ourselves comfortably in the den.

"Now, Terry, you're working with students up in Washington, D.C.?" Mr. Groover asked.

"Yes, this is my first year up there." I noticed how homey

and traditional the house looked — made you feel like staying — a comfortable feeling.

"I sure like your home," I told Mrs. Groover.

"Oh, thank you very much. Did you have much trouble finding the place once you phoned?" she asked.

"I made it real well then."

The only thing I missed as I looked around was a picture of Robert E. Lee. A bit jokingly, I asked, "I thought every southern home had a picture of Robert E. Lee?"

We all chuckled a bit and Mr. Groover commented, "Terry, we're still fighting the Civil War down here — you know!" And we all laughed.

We sat in the den for ten minutes or so, and the minute I stepped out to unload a few of my things, Mr. Groover did something behind my back that Nancy never forgot. Before we parted at Daytona, Nancy had told me, "It's really important to me what my folks think — they almost know me better than I do and I highly value their opinion." What Mr. Groover did was form the "Okay" circle with his fingers and wink in an approving way to his daughter across the room like he had never done before. Obviously, this thrilled Nancy and reassured her deeper heart that this could possibly be love and marriage ahead for her. Before saying good-night that evening, unknown to her parents, she confided to me their warm approval.

"Terry, you know what?" Nancy whispered. "My folks strongly approve of you — I mean they like you a lot. But don't tell anyone I told you."

Saturday morning we were off to Stone Mountain, a large wilderness park and preserve, where we did everything from hiking the exposed Granite Peak to rowing completely around the lake.

I don't know who teased who the most, but we rollicked with fun all day long, laughing and laughing. If I wasn't imitating a southern accent, she would be poking fun at the way I teased.

I would mimick her, "'y'all.'"

"Oh, you 'guys' are awful," she would tease in return.

I remember mentioning our relationship a time or two and how unprepared I was to find that she seemed to have a little doubt.

long, and with a rainstorm brewing, it became even longer. I barely made it back in time for the Monday afternoon meetings.

A whole new area of life had been uncovered, revealing an awesome need, one that heretofore had not seemed so large. Immediately our thoughts began to turn to the time when we could be together again but no matter how soon, it was still not soon enough. My birthday fell on that Monday and Nancy expressed:

> Well, you are now 25. You ancient old thing. I'm looking forward to spending your 26th with you and many, many more after that. You know what I was thinking about tonight that's kind of neat? Before you were ever born, or I was either, I feel like God foreordained us to be together someday.
>
> As you said, we can only look to the future in faith. He will show us the way in His time, and if *we* are willing, He will make us eager to accept what He shows us, no matter what it is.

Braced for any event? We thought so!

The grace of God! Nancy had begun to understand it; I had begun, too — it was an ingredient of strength in our relationship. So liberating! Such freedom to be ourselves with masks removed! We weren't perfect, but we did know God had loved us, totally forgiven us, and accepted us just the way we were, not on the basis of how we had or would perform. Could we not at least hope to treat each other the same way?

One big problem we faced was the fact that Nancy's life had been directed, since the time she was a little girl, toward attending and graduating from Wesleyan College, her mother's alma mater. She was in her junior year, and as graduation neared, the importance of it loomed in the minds and hearts of her parents and herself.

At the same time, it was my feeling that once you found that certain all-so-special one, you had best get married before too long.

How could I wait thirteen months to finally join completely with this adorable and receptive young "belle"? It began to bother me that, perhaps, God did want us to wait; it wasn't clear what His will was. The obstacles seemed insurmountable — the diploma, family harmony, finances, and, above all, Nancy's final agreement. I'll never forget wrestling in prayer over the matter one evening and finally totally accepting that His will, no matter what, be done, even if it meant waiting for thirteen months. Then, to further complicate our containment, Nancy wrote:

> For the past few days, I've been feeling more ready for marriage than I *ever* have before. It's like I can *picture myself* in the everyday situations of marriage as well as the romantic — for the very first time. I know it's a big step, but somehow, it seems so right that it doesn' really scare me as much and I feel more ready for responsibility.
>
> While I was observing in my little first grade today, I got real excited thinking about having our own family. Terry, I just definitely feel that we are going to get married, *and that* it's going to be *soon*. It has to be soon — don't see how I really thought of waiting a year.
>
> Something I have been thinking about, tho, is school. I want to finish. I don't care where. I'd go through ten more years of school if I could *just be with you*. Let me know what you think about it. . . .

She concluded, never failing to include my opinion as vital and valid, even after expressing her own. It was a problem to ponder, and no immediate solution seemed to focus on the horizon.

One day, about this time, something happened to show how complementary we were becoming to each other. Several problems had bounced me around, piling up complaints almost beyond endurance. I enumerated them in a letter to Nancy, and she wrote in return:

> All those things happening in one day do seem like almost too much, but as you well know, sometimes the Lord has to let this happen to strengthen our faith, if for *no* other reason. As long as everything is going along smoothly, we are really trusting, etc., but let something happen and BAM!
>
> (Then almost prophetically, as though God was writing something through her for me to come back to later — much later — she continued.)
>
> He is preparing you for something big which will involve bigger tests of faith. And He's probably giving you a small dose now so the big dose won't taste so bad later. He's kind to do this. He does care about our feelings.

So, in the midst of what seems like hell on earth and unbearable turmoil — "THANK YOU OUR LORD," we can, and must, learn to feel and say.

The words of James 1:2 must be a real part of life, if we are to survive its woes: "Count it all joy, my brethren, when you meet various trials, for you know that the testing of your faith produces steadfastness. And let steadfastness have its full effect, that you may be perfect and complete, lacking in nothing." (RSV) That problem would work out, but the question of "mama and daddy" started to dance into our minds.

After I had been to Atlanta, Nancy was able to get home a weekend or two and be with her parents and friends. But the opportunity of discussing our relationship just hadn't happened, though Nancy could feel "mama and daddy's" attitude. They were all for it, but naturally felt that after seeing so little of each other, nothing serious could have developed yet. But Nancy felt sure that our Lord had quickly given us a deep, wonderful, and solid love. She confidentially related:

> There was something I didn't tell you in my letter Sunday night. That was *how much* daddy and mama enjoyed having you at our house. (It's fun to be flattered once in a while.) Now, I don't want to inflate your ego, *but* they thought you were "so nice and easy and comfortable to be around, fit right in and just tops." That "easy to be around" thing is really a big thing, too, 'cause they've never felt that way about any of my "friends," and it does mean a lot to them.

> Grandma was snowed, and mama said she asked her about every day if we were serious.

Needless to say, our relationship had been cemented together now by a strong and indefinable glue, but the one big problem still stood in the way of marriage: Nancy's degree and the pressure to get it. Nancy concluded that same letter, however, with words almost too rich to read:

> I miss you so much, Terry, that I don't know what to do. I need you badly right now. Am tired of catching a cold and feeling so much love that I have to keep it all inside . . . you're right about those "three little words"; they don't begin to express what love is. I DO LOVE YOU though, and just plain care so much.

> Yours in Him,
> Nancy

As I was busily checking the transfer procedures to the University of Maryland, in the event that Nancy would need to finish her last year there, she had decided that the big moment had come to tell it like it was to "daddy and mama." So, slowly and conscientiously, she began to write. She knew her parents well enough to anticipate their response, but that was no reason to compromise the truth. She knew they hadn't the vaguest idea how deep our relationship had grown. Above all else, she loved them dearly and must tell them completely how she felt. She told me later that after hours of contemplation and writing, she dropped the letter in the mailbox. Then she could hardly sleep wondering what they would say.

The next evening the dorm phone rang. The intercom bleeped into Nancy's room, "Nancy, you have a long-distance call on line two — from Decatur."

7 "But Marriage Is Serious"

"Honey, this is daddy," the warm voice cheerfully announced.

> I had written and told them just how much I loved you and
> how I felt about us — WITHOUT mentioning anything definite,
> *she wrote me*. And they called just to tell me how happy they
> were about it and how much they thought of you. (This surely
> made us feel good — we wanted them to be as happy about it as
> we were.)
> I talked to daddy first and he was so sweet that I just about
> cried on the phone. He also said that they would be praying
> about it and trusting God to lead us. It was a REAL BLESSING.
> Their whole attitude was certainly an answer to prayer. As I
> said tho, I didn't tell them everything. I'll save that until you
> can talk with them too. Of course, daddy did say to take our
> time because we hadn't known each other long. I knew he
> would say that anyway.

So the drama of seeking consent to our early marriage was beginning to build, knowing the parents were determined Nancy
would finish college. We had met for the first time ten or eleven
months earlier, then in the winter by chance acquaintance we
bumped into each other again and the wheels began to turn,
then at Daytona Beach — Easter — then writing until I came
down to be with her. Here we were apart again, but fully and
deeply in love, feeling ready for marriage.

Her family thought we were a little, perhaps more, in love.
But, naturally, with school in the fall and graduation in the spring,
they all had their hearts set on Nancy's returning. Possibly, if
our love continued to prove itself, we could get married after

Nancy's graduation in a year. Yes, everyone was happy with this arrangement. I knew the lot had fallen to me to go to Nancy's father by myself and break the news.

Somehow, Nancy and I managed to convince her family that it would be good for Nancy to come up to Washington, D.C., for a couple of days before I left on a trip to California. Their reluctance gave them away only a little, as they could feel our love deepening, knowing that too much time together would push our desires towards earlier plans than theirs called for, diminishing all hopes invested into Nancy's diploma.

It was fabulous to see Nancy again as I met her at a college friend's house, with whom she was staying. We looked forward to a couple of casual days together, while in the back of my mind bobbled the sizeable question, *"Should we talk more about marriage?"*

When marriage thoughts hit your brain, one of the things you begin thinking about is a ring. I wanted to purchase secretly one she would adore, and surprise her when the big moment came. So, first, I had measured her finger in a sneaky way so that I would be prepared with the right size. By removing the ring she then wore, as we were holding hands one evening, I fit it to my own little finger, remembering how far up it went. Secondly, I had mentioned the subject in one of my letters, scheming to draw out her taste in diamonds.

I started shopping jewelry stores, this one and that one, looking for the right ring. Nancy was perfect; the ring had to be flawless. Nancy's heart was wealthy and our relationship was rich; the ring could not be small or cheap. Nancy was beautiful; the stone had to sparkle. Nancy was unselfish and not greedy; I wanted to shower her with the best possible!

The diamond I finally chose was nearly one carat in size to be placed in a four-pronged Tiffany setting of fourteen carat yellow gold. The shopping and buying had been done without so much as a hint to Nancy. Final arrangements remained undone, however, when Nancy arrived in Washington. I wanted the ring in hand as soon as possible, for when Nancy and I and her parents agreed on a date, I wanted to be prepared to place it on her finger.

The ring had to be mailed to me at Nancy's address, something rather suspenseful, for I would be there only three days, and were there a mishap, it would come to her after I had gone, destroying the element of surprise. Or, if we decided to announce our engagement while I was still there, she wouldn't be getting her ring.

On our final day in Washington, the hour zeroed in to talk about the direction our relationship would take. We had avoided the subject so that we might see how many other things we enjoyed together, but I knew that the moment had come. As we had decided to cook dinner at my apartment that evening, I laid plans for the setting and the scene.

That warm spring evening I took Nancy by the hand and lead her outdoors for a little "stroll." Behind my apartment babbled a sparkling fresh brook, running through some fragrant green foliage and a wild and piney woods. A few steps further and we were on the winding, twisting path running along the brook. A few berry blossoms were beginning to bud. The afternoon air was just turning into the evening's crisp gray chill.

We sat down on a fallen log on the bank of the stream. One ugly thing was that mosquitos, fierce big black ones, kept flying around trying to find a clear spot for an attack. We chatted for a moment or so and my heart began to beat a little faster. My hands were beginning to perspire and my throat got dry. I would begin to say, "Nancy, the time has come for us to . . ." but out would come, "It sure is pretty down here." Then my heart would beat a little faster and my throat would choke up a little more. Nancy didn't seem to be aware of any of this and innocently sat by, enthralled by the setting. Over and over in my mind I had rehearsed; it seemed like it would all be so easy and smooth. Meanwhile, the mosquitos were sharpening their spears for a choice juicy meal. Finally, the right words came.

"Nancy," I coughed, "it's time for us to talk seriously about our relationship." I faced her and looked deeply into her sparkling blue eyes, "Nancy, I definitely want you to be my wife." She seemed to accept it as calmly as though that were an already past tense fact. "Nancy, this is very serious; this is forever and ever. We will want to begin making definite plans." Serenely, she followed my every word, yet, it didn't seem to change her. She had been living already in the full confidence that this would come about.

We moved closer — arms entwined around each other. And then our lips came together in a deep, full, rich embrace.

"When do you think we should have the wedding?" she whispered into my ear.

"Aren't you going to say 'yes' first?"

"Terry —" she backed off and looked seriously into my eyes. After a pause, her whisper, "Yes — yes, of course."

We had already decided that it would be very soon, and I whispered back, "How about August — something like the seventeenth or twentieth?"

"Um — I can hardly wait — but how will that work out with you in California all summer?"

"It'll work out. I guess I'll need to talk to your dad when we get back to Atlanta."

"You know what they're going to say."

"I know, and I'm scared."

Next day we pointed the red VW south for the rendezvous with the unsuspecting family. They were all joy and smiles to have their precious daughter safely returned from her adventure. I noticed her brothers must have had the inside information, for up they shot with warm, welcome, brotherly handshakes.

Up to this point, I had said nothing to my family. Only once did I so much as offer a hint as to what was happening. They lived in the state of Washington, and two months earlier during my first trip to Atlanta, I had casually sent them a note.

"Am in Atlanta on 'business.' Having a great time!"

So I figured they were aware of something going on, but that was all I ever told them. But, now, two months later, I thought I would unload.

So the time being three hours earlier on the West Coast, I waited until the Groover household was in bed, and then I dialed the Thomas number.

"Where are you?" my mother asked.

"Atlanta."

"Well, what are you doing down there?"

"Well, I'm on my way to California and stopped in at a friend's house on the way."

"What's the weather like back there?"

"Fine. Say, is dad around?"

"Yes, do you want to talk to him?"

"Ya!"

"Okay, here he is."

I thought it might be best to lower the boom on dad first. So, after "hello's," since I was so excited I could hardly wait to tell, my first question was, "What would be the most surprising thing I could tell you?"

"I don't know."

"Try a guess."

"Uh. . . . I just have no idea."

"Well, what would you say if I told you I was getting married?"

SILENCE — then slowly:

"I'd say that would be about the best news I've heard in twenty-six years." (The time of my folks' own marriage.)

"Really, Ter, I can't believe it," I heard him say. "When did this all come about?"

About this time my mother picked up the extension phone and got tuned in to the news. At first, she was taken back, then brought up to the reality that, finally, her son was on. the countdown to the altar.

We talked on, a bit superficially at first, since they had been caught so unawares. Then they wanted to know when the wedding would be.

"Well, I'll tell you, it all depends on how things go tomorrow."

"What do you mean?"

"Well, we haven't said anything to Nancy's folks at all, and tomorrow morning I'm going down to Mr. Groover's office and talk it over."

"What do you think he will say?" mother asked.

"Well, we're not sure, but they want Nancy to finish school real bad — and at Wesleyan. If she did that, we couldn't get married for a year."

"That's awful long," dad said.

"Well, we want to get married this August, but don't change

your vacation yet, because it may be rough to be able to have it then. I mean, we don't know if they'll be behind us or not — but they sure are wonderful people — you'll like them so much."

"We'll be anxious to hear what happens," dad said.

"As I said, I'll be going down to his office in the morning."

We finally said good-bye, and I could tell the reality was already beginning to sink in.

I knew if Nancy's parents definitely said "no," we would have to abide by their decision. I knew that I stood positively in their good favor, but that they by no means wanted an early marriage.

"Mr. Groover," I said on the telephone early that next morning, with Nancy standing at my side, "this is Terry."

"Well, Terry, how are you this morning?" he cheerfully responded.

"I'm just fine. Thought I'd stop down at the office and see you this morning if you have some time."

"Sure, come on down. What time do you think you'll be here?"

"Is ten all right?"

"Ten is fine."

I don't know how many times Nancy and I had discussed how to handle the situation, but we went over it just one more time.

"Well, here goes," I said, getting ready to leave.

"Daddy won't bring it up, but will wait for you," Nancy repeated.

"I'm glad I know that, but how do I begin?"

"Terry, you'll do all right; I know you will," she answered.

I nervously looked at my watch. "I guess I better get going — I sure don't want to be late."

Nancy sent me off with a kiss and remained behind wondering about the proceedings in "daddy's office."

I don't think I've ever been more uneasy in all my life driving across town for that appointment.

And yet we had prayed together about all these matters, and although shaky, trusted Him.

I pulled up in front of the office and Mr. Groover was patiently waiting.

8 "You've Got to Talk to Daddy"

"I'm sure glad you could come down," Mr. Groover greeted me with a smile beaming across his face.

"Yes, I am too," I nervously replied with a similar big smile covering up any fear.

First, he showed me around the building, where he was district manager for a life insurance company. Finally, we entered his own large private office. He closed the door, slipped in behind his massive executive desk, sat down, spoke to his secretary over the intercom, "Mrs. Wilson, if any calls come in for me, please hold them. I'm in a private conference," and looked up to face me. I had seated myself directly across from him and found myself glancing around. The atmosphere was warm and smiles were genuine, but nothing was said for a moment or two as we sat opposite each other. I wondered how I could bring up the subject that was on my mind, but hoped that once started, the pressure that had built up inside would be released. This was one of the most daring ventures I had ever taken in my life, but my heart was so positive of the love Nancy and I had, I found myself able to brave it. Urgently, I wanted to break the tension and get started, and though it was silent and my turn to speak, I just did not quite know what to say.

Finally, I did get my mouth open, but out came something like, "Boy, your office sure is nice."

Without flinching in the least, Mr. Groover said, "Yes, we really like it."

Then, "Well . . . I suppose you know why I've come."

"No, I don't really."

"Well," I bravely announced, "it seems that Nancy and I want to get married."

For many years his feelings towards love and marriage and his children had developed. He did not have to rehearse nor stop even a moment to know exactly what he wanted to say.

"Well, I'm sure happy that you came down to see me," he warmly began. "I'd always hoped some nice young man would be thoughtful enough to come to my office and talk it over."

"I feel, Mr. Groover," I interjected, "that Nancy is yours — I mean, she belongs to you, and I wouldn't take her without your consent."

"Well, I appreciate that very much, Terry, and want you to know how much her mother and I think of you. We've thought more of you than of any friend Nancy has ever brought home.

"I'll bet you feel you know Nancy better than anyone else does right now," he continued.

I sort of nodded — I'd never really thought about it.

"Right now, though, we, as her parents, have lived with her twenty years and do know her better than you do."

I sat back and relaxed a little, and Mr. Groover was choosing his words carefully.

"Her mother and I have seen her grow up and have been with her in difficult times as well as (He sort of chuckled as some experience or other ran through his mind) good ones. We feel like she is just the finest young woman alive — she is just about as close to perfect as a person can be and still be human." Sentimentally, he added, "Yes, she'll make you a *very* fine little wife."

"Boy, I sure do know that," I put in. I thought I noticed a tear in his eye.

The subject changed a little as, "You know, Terry, how happy we are that Nancy is finishing her college education and especially that it's at Wesleyan. Maybe you've noticed, Terry, (I gulped) how special the girls seem to be down there. I've always wanted my girl to graduate from Wesleyan. It's good, too, since you have your college degree, that Nancy will have hers — that way, you'll be on the same level." (I gulped twice more.)

Nancy and I had expected this, but did not know what we

would say from here. His warm, gentlemanly southern accent continued.

"We suspected that you all going up to Washington would bring this about, but, of course, we couldn't do anything about it."

Of course, he didn't have the slightest idea how early our love had blossomed.

"You know," I interjected, "Nancy and I first felt this way two months ago at Daytona Beach, and taking Nancy to D. C. certainly affirmed our previous feelings, but by no means brought it about."

"Is that right?" he surprisedly inquired.

The tone changed just a bit as we philosophized for a moment. I remember his exact words as he discussed from his own ideal home a couple practical things that make it work well.

"There are just a few basics in marriage apart from love and sharing that you must always do," he went on as a father giving advice. "Terry, you've got to come home every night for dinner. You've also got to bring home the food, and your wife's got to cook it. No matter how you look at it, every night she has to cook dinner, and also every day has to keep your house and it's up to you to provide. And, of course, you both must be faithful." That seemed simple enough, though Nancy and I had never sat down and thought of it in just that way. You could see, though, why the father-in-law-to-be had stressed these few basic regular requirements — he had seen many a home crumble by the wayside. He knew that he didn't have to say much to us about love and steady, faithful devotion, though, for the undying attachment between Nancy and me was evident.

Then he inquired as to my plans to support his daughter and our yet unborn children. Calmly, I went over all my assets and my income, showing how we would be provided for, but also stressed that we looked to God in faith for provision. Sometimes it is difficult for folks to see how God can provide for His people's every need, but Mr. Grover seemed to have a better-than-average understanding of the Lord's bountiful supply.

Our hearts, minds, and thoughts seemed genuinely one up to this point, but as yet we hadn't discussed the specifics Nancy and

I had in mind — especially as to date of marriage. Mr. Groover seemed to assume as we chatted that there would be a post-graduation wedding in one year.

"You do want Nancy to finish college, don't you?" he brought up at this point.

"Well," I broke in, "we do, but we felt it might be sort of difficult to finish at Wesleyan."

"Oh?"

"We had hoped to get married right away."

He was set back just a little at this suggestion and didn't know quite what to say.

"By right away, just when did you have in mind?"

"We were sort of bent towards August."

A big chuckle and grin came out. "August! You just don't know what it takes to go into a wedding. We'll want to give you all a big wedding in the church, and you just don't plan something like that in two months."

Nancy and I knew this would be his suggestion, but just couldn't see how we could wait any longer.

"You see, our plan is to get married and settled this summer and then Nancy can finish college next year in Maryland."

"Well, the first thing that would happen is children would come along, and Nancy never would get finished."

I smiled and said, "Well, I think we can prevent children for a while." Mr. Groover didn't seem to know what to say.

We talked for an hour and a half and did agree on some specifics, but found even more agreement in attitude. Meanwhile, Nancy was home wondering why it was taking so long and earnestly praying for our time together. Sol and I agreed to let it ride and see what would happen, though clearly he was set on waiting until the next year after Nancy finished college at Wesleyan.

"If you just can't wait," he added, "come and see us and we'll do it up right. We'll give you the wedding and give you our blessings, but we will do everything we can to get you to just hold off. Whatever you do," he concluded, "don't run off. We'll be behind you even if you can't wait."

This note left us both happy and unified, for we both had

been able to express ourselves freely. He had expressed his blessings, but directive to wait. I had expressed Nancy's and my desire for a wedding now. But, though we did not come to any final agreement, we both felt that the other was willing to bend.

I scooted on home, to find a calm but wondering young woman who could hardly wait to get the report.

"What happened?" Nancy quickly interrogated. "Terry, why are you so happy?" She didn't find me hurrying to volunteer the information, for I was recovering from the conversation with her father myself and wasn't yet ready to pep myself up and tell it all. Her intense and stirring desire to know caused her to plead.

"Terry, tell me — please — how did it go?"

When she found out that we hadn't agreed on a date, she couldn't understand why I was so happy. She didn't realize that I was exhilarated by the fellowship and unity which had developed between my future father-in-law and myself. Then, about the time we started talking, not five minutes behind me, Sol drove up.

Without a word — just an uncontained beaming smile from ear to ear — he hopped out of his car and into the house. Quickly he was back out almost pushing Nancy's mother into the car.

"You two don't go away now — we're on our way to lunch and will be back after a while," he called.

We knew they would want to discuss things and that it would not be any easier for them, discovering our firm position. Nancy and I fixed a little lunch at home, and I carefully related to Nancy the conversation her father and I had had, emphasizing that though nothing definite was decided upon, we both felt that God would have His way in the final decision.

After we were through eating, Nancy remembered a little package that had come for me Special Delivery from Maryland while I was gone. I knew its contents and knew I would have to open the package in secret.

So I took the little wrapped item and, trying to be discreet, slipped into a spare room to uncover the cargo. The rich, green velvet case felt so good to my fingers, and I quickly popped it open to reveal the sparkling gem. I tried it on my little finger and held it up to the sun beaming in through the window. I was happy with it.

I returned to the couch in the den and sat beside Nancy with the ring in my pocket, hoping I could give it to her before leaving for California. We flicked on the television and just sort of sat there — hands entwined — patiently waiting for the parents to return. The verdict, we knew, could well be in the making right then. Though hoping for the best, we expected something between it and the worst. Of course, the worst would be to have to wait for an entire year until after graduation.

We heard a car pull into the garage and a couple of car doors slam shut. Lunch had taken them two full hours, and when Mr. Groover walked into the den, he quickly took over.

"Nancy — come upstairs, please." In a moment through the door, I heard her crying. Then he came downstairs to see me and it did not take him long to say what they had decided over lunch.

"It's important to us that Nancy finish at Wesleyan — I'll expect you to encourage her. If you all want to get married next year after she graduates, we are one hundred percent behind you, but not sooner." I suppose I sort of nodded my head as the shock sunk in, and he made his way to the door to get back to the office. A moment later Nancy appeared, red-eyed, drying her tears.

"What did he say to you?" she queried. I briefly told her and she told me what he had said to her which had been basically the same. We knew our inner feelings well — now was the time to get married, but when you honor your parents with full due respect, how do you get your way when it is directly opposed to theirs?

For the next couple of days the diamond ring stayed in my pocket while the wedding was an unmentioned subject.

With a little anxiety, not knowing exactly what to do, Nancy and I had the best time possible under the circumstances, knowing we would be forced to part in two days for an indefinite period.

The parting was terrible and one of those things you try to forget. All I can remember is seeing Nancy standing there in tears — actually both of us were blurry-eyed — as I hurried off to California with the one carat gem in my pocket. She did not even know about it.

We probably felt worse being torn apart this time than at any previous good-bye because we knew that it could be months before we would see each other again, and setting a date, either for the near future or for one year in the dim future, would have to be done through letters, often a difficult way to communicate.

We had prayed together over the indecision, as we often did over other matters, and asked the Heavenly Father for what seemed like an impossible miracle. Our request was that if God wanted us to be married soon, He would reveal it to Nancy's parents, showing them clearly that this was best for her. We felt we could see clearly, without any doubt, that it would be to the benefit of all for Nancy to leave school after three years and become a wife. Somehow, it didn't seem right that her parents didn't understand, and having our families behind us was important.

Back in my hometown, word started trickling out as we suspected it would. My folks were supposed to keep the announcement a secret until we could set the date, but in my mother's first letter she told how the word had already slipped out. She wrote about how happy she was to be getting a daughter-in-law, and that she was so joy-filled knowing that now I would have a beautiful marriage to look forward to. The slip, though, was that while at work a lady who was a friend of the family happened to ask dad, "How's Terry?"

My proud dad, without thinking, from behind a smile so bright you couldn't miss it in the dark, said, "He's getting married!"

At the age I was, people began to wonder and speculate when the day would ever come, and as soon as dad slipped, word began to spread. Within five minutes the story was relayed to my aunt who, in turn, called by grandmother. My grandmother dispatched the message to a few others, and by evening most of the circle of family and friends was informed. At home the phone was ringing off the wall with congratulatory comments and desires to get the story straight and firsthand. The next morning, my sis quickly wrote me:

> We were surprised about you getting married. But when I think about it, I'm not too surprised. One time you wrote you

had been to Georgia on "business," and I thought the quotes meant a girl! We are real anxious to meet Nancy.

We would *really*, really like to be there on the big day. Georgia is a long way and costs quite a bit to get there, yet the time is still a ways off.

Oh, yes, mother has it all figured out how everyone can get there except for the finances. I thought this was quite funny — she is really quite excited.

A favorite cousin had to add her bit to the excitement, too, with:

> Yes, I have heard of your "adventures" in that fair state of Georgia, but not enough to satisfy my "young maiden's innocent curiosity." Besides, nothing beats the horse's mouth — so, come on cousin — GIVE!!!!

A good pal who had been on the inside from the beginning wrote:

> Still waiting final word on your big plans. Where and When — (I know the "why" and I hope the "who" remains the same.) Say, give Nancy a big kiss for me, too.

When your dad writes you, it has to be a very special occasion. This was special enough for mine, and since he wrote so seldom, his words were especially meaningful to both Nancy and me.

> I am real anxious for you to come home with your bride-to-be. She sounds like a real nice, sensible girl and I am sure if you say she is tops that is the ultimate. I shall be happy for both of you. May God further bless you in the love of a lifelong companion.
>
> You certainly have my most hearty blessings and good wishes.

About that time, Nancy and I had been doing some thinking about some events that were happening in the world which seemed to be predicted in the Bible. It was clear to us that Jesus Christ would return to the earth in the same way as He had left. It also seemed highly probable that His return as foretold in the Bible could happen at any time in our generation. We thought about this and agreed, though, that our foremost desire — to get married — possibly overshadowed our desire to see our Christ —

though we did not want it to. Early in the summer, I wrote to Nancy:

"We are certainly living in exciting times and I look forward to seeing the Lord so much. Won't that be wonderful?"

But we had to admit that we wanted to experience marriage too, though in our deeper minds we knew that no matter what our preconceptions of the afterlife, or what our state of being at the time it came to us, either through His return or upon our death, we would immediately be totally thrilled and happy. We would have no regrets from the past nor dissatisfaction with the present, no matter what the circumstances surrounding the event.

The big obstacle that continued to loom before us, however, was the consent of Nancy's parents. And not just consent — we desired total backing and enthusiasm, that the occasion might bring great joy to all. I arrived in California, two thousand miles away, with only letters to keep us in touch with transpiring events and each other's feelings.

It was comforting to get Nancy's card right after I left, as these questions lingered:

My parents were very sympathetic and sweet after you left. More on that later.
I wish everyone could have someone like you — *just like you.* They just don't know what they're missing.

Even though the folks strongly approved of our relationship, it seemed that their desire for her to finish college at Wesleyan was just as strong, and I had to write to her as a result:

When? Nancy, I've asked the Lord to arrange for it soon, but am not clear at all that it is His will — so only registered the request. Yet, again, it would be good for you to have your degree.

So, there we hung in the balance. What was right? When was best? Which was most practical? From the opposite viewpoint, I also had to quickly include:

On the other hand you may *resent* the degree, your parents, and a big wedding if you are forced to wait against your will.

And Nancy's augmenting thoughts further confused the issue:

For all practical purposes, I think we should wait until June, but then I don't see how we can wait. So, the question is — does the Lord want us to be practical, or to do what our hearts tell us to do?

We knew that we could tough it out by sheer determination for a full year, if we were positive that that was God's will, yet, the looming problem wasn't solved.

9 Final Decision

Throughout this distressingly indecisive period, letters and reactions taught us more about each other and our relationship.
Nancy wrote, the day I left for California:

My darling,

Only the Lord can convey to you how much I need you and
want you right now. The day has been long and I keep thinking that soon I will see you, but you aren't here. I have thought
of you a million times. . . . I am feeling more and more like my
place is with you — wherever you go and whatever you do.

It does something to a guy to have a woman back him up and
treat him like a king — it makes him feel and act with confidence
and ability he never knew he had. I *could* write back:

My life has been so enriched and made more confident as a
result of our love — your love for me — and has made me more
of a man.

It is important that a woman treat her man as though he were
the only and very best man in the whole world. If she does,
he will behave like the best, and thus she will have a terrific
husband. If she continually scrutinizes nothing but his faults,
holding them up before him, he will become more self-conscious,
thus multiplying these weaknesses. I began to appreciate Nancy
more and more as I saw what was happening to me on the basis
of her treatment.

One day, though, she was afraid I was becoming a little more
prominent than Christ in her life and wrote:

I was concerned that I was putting you before Him. He seemed to show me, however, that the way I feel is perfectly natural and necessary if I am to be your wife, and that He is still first but that a lot of what I learn about Him will come through you — not all — but a lot.

If only wives would treat their husbands with the respect they give Christ! Nancy was giving me complete honor in every way, which is the way Christ meant it to be.

I found it easier and more natural as our relationship developed to repeat and repeat with crescendo: "I love you, I love you, I love you." She found it easier to write in return glowing praises not only of her beau, but our relationship, such as:

And now He has made me for you so that through our life together we can serve Him in a *special* way. Terry, I really do feel that He has a *unique* purpose for our union — because I know He has chosen you as one of His special workmen. I feel privileged and blessed that He has chosen me to stand beside you.

While feeling a bit tipsy and, perhaps, a tad off balance because of love, at times the realistic side loomed into focus too, so that we could also keep our minds a bit practical. Nancy told me:

Terry, I'm beginning to realize that a marriage with real oneness between a man and a woman is *rare*. Praise the Lord for what He has given us. He has taught me so much and how thankful I should be.

How necessary understanding is even when there isn't an explanation for someone's behavior; how very *complete* giving on the part of both partners; and how important it is to be *realistic* going into a marriage.

Thank God for love — His love — out of which grows patience, trust, and understanding.

Meanwhile, the decision of when the marriage was to take place hung over us. In California, I had breakfast one morning with Dick Ballew, my regional director, and we discussed the matter.

"Dick, what do you think we should do?"

"Does the family believe in Christ?"

"Yes, definitely, and they are all for the marriage. They are just resolute on Nancy's finishing college."

"What would they do if you went ahead?"

"They would be behind us, but there would still be some sorrow and hidden sad feelings."

"I wouldn't tell you what to do — you do as the Lord shows you — but my suggestion would be to wait."

I told Nancy what Dick said and also reiterated our original prayer:

> I have prayed, Nancy, that unless your parents were not only in agreement, but felt it best we marry now, that we would wait. I feel, Nancy, that is His will.
>
> June is only eleven months away. Time goes so fast.
>
> Yet, our Father, by His infinite power, could instill in your wonderful parents the view or vision that it would be best for us to marry now.

Nancy was helping in the family at home and wrote:

> I love you, Terry, and want to marry you *as soon as* possible. Tonight I was helping with supper and thinking how much I'd rather be cooking for you. I'd rather do everything for you. I just want to be with you.

We knew that our Father in Heaven was also concerned about the date. He had brought us together at a specific time months earlier, and our fruitless anxiety would not change the date one way or the other. So, the issue boiled down to trusting Him completely, though we needed to learn to rest and relax in that reliance. Confidently relaxing wasn't easy, but any test of faith that reaches above past experience always requires a little groping before rediscovering faith's simplicity. Maybe this is why God did not reveal the date until He did.

Love — so unsheltered — so revealing. When you come to love another person as I had Nancy, you recognize again that the power to love is experienced only through Christ. You find yourself able to let that person get close to you — that is, become a part of your deepest inner self. You are not afraid of what they will find because you know that in the final analysis, they will experience warm, tender, unfailing love because you are a new, wonderful person in Christ. So you fall in love, and with Christ's love as the foundation, you find a wonderful unselfish giving from the other person, and also from yourself, such as you never imagined possible. Sure, old behavioral patterns that aren't so good may crop up at times, but, nevertheless, Christ is still the Lord.

It was the middle of the summer when the date finally was settled — a date Nancy and I and Mr. and Mrs. Groover found completely satisfactory.

Dave, a good friend of mine, and myself were rooming together in California at the time. I had often shared developments with Dave, and now he laughed joyfully as I read him this latest letter from Nancy. We barely believed our eyes and ears.

"Dave, do you realize what this means?" I said, in the midst of our excitement.

"I know, man, you'll be married this year!"

"Can you believe it?"

Mr. and Mrs. Groover had seen, as the summer wore on, that Nancy could not live another year without me. They saw very clearly that the best thing for Nancy was marriage. Best for Nancy and best for them. It was seeing this that prompted their change of attitude. So, Nancy would not be finishing at Wesleyan.

I had written Nancy the same day she wrote me of identical feelings. Unbelievable! Nancy and I could barely contain our anticipation and excitement.

That little ring I was carrying would soon find its rightful place on her left hand.

We started counting the 120 odd days until the magic one, either Friday, November twenty-fourth, or Saturday, November twenty-fifth. It was ironic later that our minds were focused in on November twenty-fifth, the day which actually followed our wedding.

"All I can think about lately is November twenty-fifth."

I jotted back:

"Were the plans complete and the wedding ready — the guests in place — you adorned — I'd marry you *NOW!*"

Nancy returned:

"You really have become my best friend — besides being my spiritual leader and my 'lover' — and I miss you."

Sometimes our thoughts drifted to philosophizing a bit about marriage. A marriage must include more than love. The Bible teaches that in Christ we actually love everybody — even girls and women who aren't a fellow's wife. In an ideal marriage, there exists a friendship and affinity, something more than love, where the two who've become one enjoy each other and doing things together that one would do only with his best friend. They mutually enjoy interests outside the house and the realm of love, and at times, perhaps, almost pal around in these discussions and activities.

Also, the ideal home must exist in part in the invisible spiritual realm. The spiritual realm brings a deep indefinable cement into marriage that glues it together so solidly and permanently that it is impossible to be pried apart. And, too, the husband is and must be the natural spiritual leader.

Now we began to anticipate marriage as it would unfold — often anticipating the setting up of a nifty newlyweds' apartment and experiencing the fresh joys that would follow the wedding itself.

Nancy began to ask me what my taste was in china, silver, and crystal, and all at once I had to try to learn about these things. Like most guys, I never noticed what I ate from, only the food.

The in-law situation was turning out to be ideal from both angles, too. I felt that Nancy's family — parents, brothers and sister — was the most wonderful family I had ever met. I respected them from the start and began to love them dearly. I knew that they felt good towards me, too, and any difficulty they had had in anticipating their daughter's walking the aisle that year was quickly vanishing. They wrote me how proud they were of us both and how happy they were with the marriage and the date.

Even though my parents and fiancé had never met, they also began to share a mutual love and admiration. Nancy wrote to me:

> I got the most precious letter from your mother today. Oh, Terry, she sounds so perfect — it is all so perfect that it brought tears to my eyes. I feel like I know her already — she was so warm and open. She told me how she had always been praying for

the right one for you all — it all sounded so much like my own mother and I know we're going to have a wonderful time when we go up to meet them. I pray that we can really become close and will see them often.

Meanwhile, my bride-to-be continued to reveal pleasant surprises to the already too-far-impressed groom-to-be. Nancy felt that too often brides were the focal point of the wedding, basking in the limelight while the groom rested in the shadows. She wrote:

All along, I've not only wanted you to be a part but *the major part*. I cannot stand the bride getting all of the attention. All of it, plans, presents, etc., belong just as much to you as to me.

What more could a fellow want than a girl like that? And, now, we would be together again *soon* — and this time not for three days or even ten — but six weeks. We knew it would not be easy, this close togetherness all the time, feeling such a great desire to be married, yet, often being separated for hours and nights. We knew that being engaged would, perhaps, bring hardships.

As Nancy was preparing for her trip to California, she experienced a rugged, little, thorny test such as makes one's faith die or grow — proving it to be real or false. She had had a turn or two at encouraging me through these kinds of times, and now I had a turn at helping her.

He will use anything He can to test our faith, thus causing growth. What faith would it take if the situation were different? Probably none, thus missing out on the resultant blessings. I get, it seems, so I almost expect multitudes of complications in anything I do. They are always (nearly) there.

So it seemed that we were a rich addition to each other's lives in standing by with encouragement as a problem or frustration or a "down" experience passed our way.

Nancy was soon coming to California for some training and to be with me, and wrote some words just before she left that continued to dazzle me:

Tonight it really hit me how lucky — blessed — I am, and I thank our Father for bringing us together *now* so that I no longer have to be incomplete. So that my life can be lived to the fullest.

Why should He bless me? It is all so perfect. As Helen said, last week, it is all that I have always wanted and prayed for — you, serving our Lord, serving Him as your wife. Even the little things are perfect, too. I have prayed for you all my life. You are truly from God and in you He has answered my every need and desire.

As the final days before she was to fly to California dragged on, I finished my last letter:

Please let me know when you'll be arriving. Oh, Nancy — to see you — touch you — yes — again!!!!
Goodnight, my love — and see you in six days. It has been about forty-seven.

I love you — precious,
Terry

Nancy's flight was to arrive at Los Angeles International at ten fifty-nine. It took exactly one hour and a half to get there from San Bernardino, and I did not want to be late. But, somehow, I fooled around too long getting everything ready and left to meet Nancy not at nine, as planned, but nine-thirty. I knew it would be close. I could just picture my bride-to-be stepping off the plane, searching, and finding no one to meet her.

10 The Ring

When I nosed off the ramp at the airport exit, it was ten-fifty. Nancy's plane was arriving at ten fifty-nine. I was held up at a couple of red lights and finally parked the car at ten fifty-three. Watching the time anxiously, I tore up to the United Airlines desk, asked at which gate Nancy's plane was to arrive, and ran — sport coat waving — tie flapping — down the concourse to the receiving area. The airport clock registered ten fifty-seven — two minutes to spare.

The plane was about ten minutes late, however, giving me an interval to chew toothpicks and pace the floor. But, man, when that plane dropped in and chauffered my Georgian brunette beauty to the terminal — what a sight! Over seven weeks had gone by — our longest separation — and was it ever wonderful to be together again.

"I just can't believe it's really you," I heard myself say.

"Oh, Terry, I can't believe it either — I just can't believe it."

"Honey, I love you," my heart and mouth whispered as we met with a kiss. Nancy was embarrassed in the terminal with people around.

"How was your flight?"

"Oh, just fine."

"I just barely made it here in time."

"You did? Did it take you long?"

"An hour and a half."

"Oh, Terry, I still can't believe we're together."

Talking rapidly, we picked up her luggage, walked to the car, and left the airport.

I suppose it took a while to get readjusted to being together again after being apart for so long, while thinking constantly of each other and anticipating life together; it took a little time for us to comprehend the reality of being hand in hand.

Excitement was high and nerves were sensitive when the red VW began to escort us along the scenic Southern California coastline, the long way back to Arrowhead Springs. South of Marineland we found a little restaurant and pulled in for dinner. We ordered nothing but the best — top sirloin. I didn't give Nancy a chance to try to order anything less expensive. We had so much to talk about and discuss, though, that eating seemed almost irrelevant. Most of all, we basked in the reality of being together again.

Driving back in the heavy freeway traffic, we were slowed to a crawl and eventually found out why. Somehow, there had been a terrible car crash — the kind you only hear about or read of in the paper — the kind you never imagine happening to you. We couldn't tell how badly people were hurt or if any had been killed. We felt badly for a while, but as usual, not knowing the persons involved, it became an incident soon forgotten.

"If we were ever hit in this thing, there sure isn't much protection," I mentioned to Nancy. However, we felt perfectly safe cruising along the highway, our seat belts buckled.

Nancy was coming to Arrowhead Springs to receive introductory training in the collegiate organization I had been a part of, for as my wife she would be considered a full-time staff member, which required the three-week course. Arrowhead Springs was a beautiful, 1800-acre tract used formerly as a resort, including swimming pools, steam caves, plush hotel, and like luxuries. I was helping give the training, so the situation was ideal. After the meeting that evening, we strolled through some palm trees away from the hotel and came to the steps of an old dark tennis court. It was warm and the smell of blossoms pervaded the air.

As yet, Nancy had said nothing about a ring, and I hadn't mentioned it either, except for a hint in a letter one week earlier. When the moment came, I wanted to surprise her. However, the ring was still locked in the vault at the bank. I had a plan, but it did not include that first evening's reunion. As we peered out over the city, the lights of San Bernardino were exceptionally clear to us on the hillside.

We were especially thankful to our Father for joining us together once again and making the way for us to get married in November. So, with emotion and excitement, we joined together in looking to Him.

"Our Father," I began, "I'm so grateful tonight that Nancy — the fabulous girl you've given me — is by my side. After all this waiting, it hardly seems possible, Father, and we just don't know what to say or how to express ourselves."

"I, too, Father," Nancy prayed, "I want to say how grateful I am for Terry and that I can be with him again. Thank you for showing my folks Your will and that now we are *all* so happy with the plans.

"And, Father, we trust that during this time of being together here that You will have Your complete way. Show us anything — teach us anything — just whatever would be Your will. And we know that loving is Your will — so we are thankful that You have given us new life, and that we can be loving in all our ways — with others — with each other — and to ourselves."

We quietly talked to each other for several hours. I guess I squeezed Nancy's hand so tightly, being so glad to have her back, that our hands nearly bolted themselves inseparately together.

"My folks are sure anxious to meet you, sweetheart," I told her.

"I know, and I'm looking forward to getting to Bellingham." After our three-week stay in California, we planned on driving north to Bellingham, Washington, my hometown, before Nancy returned to make final plans for the wedding.

"I wonder if we'll get used to being together for six whole weeks," Nancy said.

"We'll probably get tired of each other or fight a lot — or something," I put in.

"You don't mean it — what?" Nancy quickly sat up.

"Ha, ha, ha," I started laughing, and then she did, too, and we were on our way for a joyful six weeks — but often with serious moments, too.

The next day the five or six hundred of us at Arrowhead Springs went to the beaches of Southern California to enjoy the sunshine and surf.

I felt a little tense that morning, and couldn't understand why I wasn't as psyched up over Nancy as the night before. I guess high emotions such as our first day together in weeks are often followed by a swing of the pendulum.

My plan with the ring called for giving it to Nancy at a time when we could announce our engagement publicly. Sunday evening had been impossible, but I knew that Monday evening an ideal setting and occasion would present itself.

So, Monday morning on the way to the beach, I stopped for gas at a service station about one-half block from the bank where the ring was. As gas was being pumped into the car, I quickly slithered around back of the station and ran the half block to the bank. Inside, I threaded my way to the safety deposit box and grabbed the ring. I streaked back to the side of the service station and casually strolled out to the car in view of Nancy. As I slid into the car, I slipped the green velvet case under the seat, without the least suspicion from Nancy.

Returning late that afternoon from the beach, I knew that to complete the plan I would have about half an hour to get Nancy to a secluded location, give her the ring, and ask the head of our organization to announce the engagement at the evening's meeting.

So, quickly, with "I'll be back at six-thirty sharp, honey, and maybe we can go for a little stroll before the meeting," and "I'll be waiting in the lobby," we parted.

Time would not have mattered so much, except that to talk to Bill Bright we would have to be at the meeting early. Otherwise, the announcement would have to be postponed.

When I pulled up in front of the hotel at six-thirty and hopped out, I carried in my hand a little brown bag of "prunes," only unknown to Nancy, the prunes had been removed.

Nancy was chatting with someone in the lobby, trying to explain why she was taking the three-week training, and somehow

I had to get her away quickly without arousing suspicion. It was nearly twenty minutes to seven — twenty minutes to accomplish the mission. I knew of an old trail that led to an ideal setting overlooking a broad valley.

Further complications blocked our path, however. The moment we started out onto the lawn, we bumped into a good friend of mine and his wife who had just returned from Europe. They had never met Nancy, but had heard of her and looked forward to getting a chance to become acquainted. Somehow, we soon broke away and were confronted with another complication — another friend. This time it was a former girl friend of mine who wanted to meet Nancy too. I held tightly onto the little brown sack as we chatted for a moment, finally excused ourselves and headed towards the old winding trail. Unbeknown to us, however, an even larger complication lay waiting. Just as we approached a pile of rocks, a large black snake slithered onto the trail. He stopped right in the middle, raised his head, turned it our way, and gave us a dirty look. We were only about eight feet from the serpent, and I quickly pulled Nancy back.

"Oh, Terry, what is it?" her mouth leaped open.

"Oh, just a snake," I said casually, but moved into action. Quickly I picked up a rock, while handing Nancy the little brown bag.

"Look out, Terry!" she cried.

"Don't worry," I bravely assured her. I guess the snake only wanted to have some fun, though, for when he saw how serious we were — Nancy backing away with the little brown bag and me arming for battle — he sneaked into the rocks to be lost forever.

Nancy handed back what she thought was only a bag of prunes, I smiled and laughed under my breath, and we continued on our stroll.

The orange sun had just set as we approached the overlook, and the brown California dusk wrapped its arms around the ideal panoramic view for this once-in-a-lifetime occasion. I could hardly wait to see Nancy's eyes when the gem was revealed.

Just as soon as we were seated, I boldly said, "Well, sweetheart, let's see what's in the sack." Upon spying the green velvet case,

Nancy was speechless, and it was one of the few times I saw her lose composure. I held it for a few seconds, then said, "Nancy, are you sure you want this?"

"Yes."

"Any doubt at all?" She was staring at the case.

Then, shakily, "No."

"Well, me neither, that I want to give it to you, I mean. Do you want to see what's inside?"

She was speechless. Slowly, I started to pry open the cover. I had it open about one-fourth of the way when it popped — it popped open to reveal to the one I loved the gem I was so proud to give. It glistened and sparkled — even brighter than the evening — almost as though it had a little light down inside the case flashing through the stone.

We gazed at it for a moment or two. Then, without saying a word, with my right hand I removed it from the case, and with my left I took hold of Nancy's. Slowly, I put the ring up to her hand and touched it to her finger. My hands were shaking too. I slid it past each knuckle to its final resting place. And then Nancy looked at me.

"Oh, Terry, how did you know what I liked. It's just what I wanted — just exactly my favorite — I just love it — and, oh — Terry — thank you." And her eyes kept gazing at me, never glancing at the stone. I will never forget that moment, for Nancy's real self was totally exposed. If she had ever acted before, she could not now. I felt like the most honored king in the world, for Nancy praised me — and not just for the ring — but just because I was me. As she stared at me, she came as close to crying as she could and still not do it.

"Terry, I just don't know what to say — oh, I just love it — it's just exactly what I like," she softly but with enthusiasm whispered.

"How did you know? And it fits, too."

"You don't know how cagey I can be," I grinned. "Now, if you're dissatisfied at all, we can easily trade it, since you didn't get to help pick it out."

"Oh, no — it couldn't be more perfect." The amazing thing was that as we talked she still did not look at the ring, but continued to look at me. I glanced down at her petite hand and it was shaking slightly from excitement. Of course, I could not have felt better or been happier seeing her reaction and knowing how much she liked the choice.

Time was creeping upon us, and it was time to leave the lovely setting and make our way to the meeting where the announcement of our engagement would be given.

Bill Bright just happened to be driving up the road to the auditorium as we walked by, so I flagged him down and he invited us to ride along. He had never met Nancy. "Nancy, you know Bill, and Bill, this is my fiancé, Nancy Groover.

"You remember that you said you would announce our engagement?"

"Yes, Terry, do you want it done tonight?"

"That would be great — I just gave Nancy her ring."

He had seen so many romances, courtships, engagements, marriages, and children born around him that this was almost everyday routine. He never got tired of it, though, and loved to be a part. In fact, as he saw how happy and excited we were, he got a little excited too.

For the next two hours, we sat through the meeting in the second row, squirming a bit and whispering a little, hardly able to contain our anticipation. We were thrilled to finally have everything settled and the evidence on her finger. Now we wanted everyone to know. Bill was the only other person in the room who knew what was coming, and occasionally he would glance our way from the platform with a twinkle in his eye.

The meeting ended — we were almost afraid Bill was going to forget to do it, but he didn't; I think he just wanted to play with us a little. Then he began the longest little speech.

"There's a man here tonight I just wanted to say something about." He always delayed these special announcements to get everyone in the audience especially curious as to who was getting married. "He's been on the staff for over two years," he went on, with far more words than necessary, dragging the announcement out. Then he hit it. "Terry Thomas has asked Nancy Groover to be his wife, and she said 'yes,'" and applause began.

We stood and took a bow and suddenly it was all over — except the congratulatory comments which followed.

When we reached Nancy's folks on the phone, they, too, were caught up in the jubilation. "Hello, son," I heard Nancy's mother say. And from the extension phone, I heard her father say, "We want you to know how proud we are of you two — and how happy we are with everything."

"That sure makes us feel good — it is going to be so good to be a part of the family."

"Oh, we're the ones who are blessed," Jane said.

"When are you coming home?" they wanted to know.

"We'll be going to Bellingham from here, and then Nancy will fly home in September."

"When will you be down," they wanted to know, "so we can show you off?"

"It'll be over two months," I told them. This information was not new, of course, but did give us something to talk about. It sure felt good that they were so enthused about our marriage.

Days rolled by and our engagement was wonderful. Often we would go for a swim in the evening or just a walk, always enjoying whatever we did. One practical thing we often did was pause for a few minutes to pray together before saying good-night; it helped bind our deeper inner selves into one. It wasn't a rule to us — we missed often — but something that would happen spontaneously.

Saying good-night as the three weeks moved along was not easy and almost put Nancy into a bad mood on several occasions. Communication between wasn't always ideal either — in fact sometimes we felt estranged. I guess that is one of the small trials engagements must go through as two strangers grow to intimacy. But it wasn't really a problem — just something that happened and was soon forgotten. However, the excitement over the future made us especially anxious for the day of departure.

My younger sister had flown down for a few days as a part of her vacation and so the three of us finally slipped off on our way to the north. The sunrise was still behind the hills as I approached the Arrowhead Springs Hotel at four in the morning to pick up the girls. There we were — tons of baggage, three adults, and a VW. One hour of packing later, we zoomed off the grounds.

We had two goals that day: one, to get across the Mojave Desert before the noonday heat, and two, to see Yosemite National Park before dark.

Even in the early morning hours, the desert was quite hot, and as we got to Yosemite we discovered a pleasant cool contrast. Nancy especially was delighted with the high mountains and deep gorges, having never seen the craggy peaks we boast of in the West.

"I've never seen such things," Nancy explained as we approached the high altitude summit at Yosemite Pass.

"Oh, this is nothing," my sister and I assured her, trying to show off our everyday attitude over these heights. And the water tasted so good when we stopped by a gushing stream for a drink. The outdoors was just what we liked — room to turn around and grab a breath of fresh air without intrusion. How good, too, to know and honor the Creator of this marvelous creation. With this panoramic beauty before us, we remembered for a moment how much more beautiful it must be to actually step into His eternal Heaven. Yes, how good to one day see Him face to face.

Soon we were on our way again, passing through Northern California and Oregon into Washington, the Evergreen State of the Northwest.

Nancy was looking forward to meeting her parents-in-law-to-be, but I was even more thrilled to be bringing this Georgia gem home. And my dad and mom were more excited, probably, than I.

So proudly, with anticipation, I turned into the driveway and drove up to the door of my home.

11 Hikin', Fishin', 'n a Girl in Hip Boots

For just a moment everything was quiet; then suddenly my folks appeared. My mother recalled the momentous occasion later:

"I can still see that day as though it were just last week. First of all, it was a beautiful day, and the yard was so green and pretty. Maybe it just seemed like an extra special day, as we were expecting you kids, and, of course, I was excited about that.

"You pulled up in front in your shiny, red VW. And, of course, Dad and I went right out to meet you. You and Nancy were in the front seat, and do you remember how loaded down you were? You were all eager to get out of the car and stretch.

"Nancy! Instantly it seemed as if I had always known her. She was already like one of the family. She was wearing one of those new pant dresses, and I was so surprised she was so small.

"The reason I think I felt like I knew her was because she acted so natural. Even at a time like this, where she was meeting her future in-laws, she didn't 'put-on.' Her hair had been blowing in the wind, but she didn't even let it bother her.

"Nothing special was said, anymore than we greeted and kissed all of you.

"I had dinner ready, and we sat at the table and visited for several hours."

Before Nancy left the Pacific Northwest, she saw about as much as one could see and still sleep nights. Our activities carried us from the rangy, snow-capped Cascades, to outings on deep, blue Puget Sound, and an enchanting visit to Canada lying just across the border. We missed a lot, too, for there was more than could be packed into one trip, but we knew there would be a next time.

The day before Labor Day, Nancy and Dad and I went out salmon fishing from my folks' summer place on Puget Sound. Dad was the lucky one that day, landing our only salmon, but that was all we needed. "Play him in, play him in," I kept telling him, and Nancy would laugh with excitement as the silver would pull the line from one side of the boat to the other. This was all new to her, and it was a tossup for my attention between coaching Dad with the salmon and keeping Nancy from jumping in after it.

"Hold him — hold him — hold him," Nancy squealed when the fish broke water and splashed near the boat.

"Take it easy, dad, tire him out," I coaxed. I'm sure all this advice did a lot of good; at least, we felt that it did. Finally, we netted the choice catch, which turned out to be more than our appetites could hold the next day.

In the morning, after breakfast, we fired up the smoker outdoors to barbeque the salmon as a special treat for the southern addition to the family.

Next on the agenda was paddling around near shore in the low tide to get our fresh crab salad to go with the salmon for dinner. I don't know when Nancy was ever cuter — dressed in a pair of hip boots about four sizes too large, with one of my old red sweat shirts dangling — she had that feminine look out of place as she tromped down to the boat determined to get crab. She turned out to be even more excited about crabbing than salmon fishing. We pushed the boat out over the green seaweed by poling with our oars on the bottom. Dad was poling us along, and Nancy and I each had a hoop at either end of the boat to hook the crab.

"There's one," Dad quietly pointed and tried to nose the boat so we could reach him. I placed my hook down and off it scuttled, scampering on all six legs. I chased and beat and reached, but he made it to the cover of seaweed. Soon we spotted another, again on my end of the boat. I quickly hooked him and landed him in our bucket.

"That's one!" I exclaimed, anticipating about six.

"I see one over there — there he is," Nancy gleefully exclaimed. So we nosed the boat in that direction. It turned out to be just a dead crab shell, however, but soon Nancy had her chance with a live one and nearly fell overboard in her determination to hook him.

"I see one," she called, a little calmer this time, "and it's crawling!" After a mild chase and effort to hook it, Nancy proudly pulled it into the boat — but turned quickly to look for another. We did finally get our five or six which made excellent fresh crab salads.

Crab and salmon weren't enough, however, and so we quickly piled back into the boat and made our way to a secret oyster bed we knew about. What would taste better in the evening, after dinner had digested, than oyster stew from freshly picked oysters?

Against the strong-running low tide, we sailed and secretly slipped up to a beach on an island near the bed. Carefully and quietly we began searching the shore for the salt-water shells. Soon we found several — more than we could carry — and in a matter of minutes we left the island with about forty choice oysters.

To top off all the fresh seafood, mother had prepared fresh blueberry pies from berries they had picked high in the mountains only a few weeks earlier. And to complement the pie, Nancy and I spent about an hour stirring up some of that expensive but delicious homemade ice cream. We took turns on that old ice cream maker — one of us packing ice and salt — the other turning the crank.

The weather did its part, too, in providing ideal conditions in the midst of a world we forgot was filled with tragedies and problems destroying perfection.

Nancy and I found an aged, weather-beaten, gray log on the beach just the right size to sit on, and as the orange sun was just falling over the ocean, we relaxed and enjoyed the peace and serenity.

"We can really appreciate a day like today, honey," I quietly rambled, "because so many days we are out in the world where we can't enjoy this relaxed fun and beauty."

"I know — just think," Nancy replied.

"So many people are starving and miserable," I continued, "and we have been given so much. But without Christ, all we've done today is empty. Yet, life is full with Him in our lives, no matter what we are doing. So I guess it's useless to worry about our circumstances."

"Isn't it silly how we have a tendency to get caught up in what's around us — I mean forgetting that our Lord towers above it all."

We sat quietly a few moments.

"Just think, sweetheart, someday we will step out beyond that sunset and right into His presence," I whispered. Nancy just sat there and stared with a faraway look.

Soon our bikes carried us back through the shadows to the end of a most exciting and perfect day.

About this time, announcements of our engagement began to appear in the newspaper society columns. One of the most interesting came from the *Orlando Sentinel* which has a circulation of over 100,000 in that rapidly growing area. True to southern tradition, and in spite of the large city, they managed to retain the homespun flavor.

> Time passes so quickly. Seems only yesterday Jane and Sol were here with their four youngsters, Nancy, Tommy, Rob, and Mary — hobnobbing with all the young marrieds and participating in all of Our Town's cultural and civic activities. But it wasn't "just yesterday," it was four or five years ago they moved to Atlanta — and now comes word Nancy is to be married.
>
> Nancy and Terry Clifford Thomas, son of Mr. and Mrs. Clifford George Thomas of Bellingham, Washington, met at Daytona Beach — romance blossomed — and now the wedding date is set for the day after Thanksgiving.
>
> Nancy was an outstanding student at Wesleyan in Macon for three years, and her fiancé is a graduate of Western Washington State College, Bellingham, Washington, and is now on the staff of Campus Crusade for Christ. No doubt there'll be innumerable Orlandoans going up for the wedding.

A wonderful letter came for me that week from Nancy's mother, expressing well the warmth and love of their home which had made Nancy what she was. Nancy's parents wanted to make certain that we knew how good they felt about the forthcoming marriage.

> Terry, we do not want you to feel that you owe us an apology for Nancy's not returning to Wesleyan. Some weeks ago, we realized this was not best and tried to relieve Nancy's mind about it. We did suggest that some time spent in school might be beneficial — perhaps a quarter or two here in Atlanta — but as Sol expressed it, Nancy is convinced she is doing the right thing and there comes a time for each of us when that is what we must do.
>
> Please try to understand that any hesitancy on our part was not to interfere with your and Nancy's plans *or* the Lord's will for you both.
>
> We will really be anxious to have you visit *us* again, Terry, whenever you can come. For the past several years, we have prayed that God would provide a Christian man with Christian traits for Nancy, and He has certainly answered our prayers. We sincerely and lovingly welcome you into our family.

They surely missed her, too, at this time when she was away from home. But, still, they were happy that we had this opportunity, and especially that Nancy could get to know my parents well, for they would soon be her family, too.

"Nancy, it'll be impossible to ever tell you how much you mean to me," I told her over breakfast one morning.

"Oh, Terry, won't it be neat to be together *all the time!*" she replied.

Indeed, being engaged wasn't easy, but perhaps it was a good test of our endurance, for we were caught and compressed between the pressures within and the pressures without. One of the pressures I felt most was a desire to be alone. Not often, but occasionally, I just wanted to get away. It was new to me to be with someone so much. I loved Nancy, there was no question about that; I just wasn't used to being with her so much. I didn't see imperfections in her that bothered me, either; I just felt at times that I wanted to be by myself and couldn't. Yet, I continually found a deep source of strength in the bottomless well of our Christ who had told us that if we drank the water He gave, we would never thirst again.

Being realistic, I suppose that sex is one of the most anticipated joys of an engaged couple; Nancy and I knew each other's desire without talking about it a lot. We knew that if we were to dwell on this powerful subject, with the strong love we had, it could lead to an unhealthy atmosphere. It was never a question to us as to how far we should go. We knew that being too personal would only lead us on.

Guilt feelings were marvelously foreign to us. We knew, though, that our Father's forgiveness for our sin was total and complete because of His Son's death on the cross, and we knew also that should we, or anyone else, fall short of God's best in this way, there would *always* be forgiveness — not cheaply, and not on the basis of our sorrow or repentance, but at Christ's expense on the cross where God had poured out His wrath once and for all for those who received His Son.

And we appreciated His power over temptation, but knew that should we slip, it would be because we had lost sight of His grace, and that the slip would only serve to drive us closer to Him who loved us, giving us a new glimpse of the unconditional love He had. But, thanks to Him, we somehow never faltered. This way, we were positive, was the most practical.

In between all of the wildlife hikes and outings, one evening we were privileged to travel across the border to enchanting British Columbia. At the peak of Grouse Mountain, a lofty, cliff-shingled mountain overlooking the sparkling and picturesque city of Vancouver, rested a plush and famous restaurant.

One afternoon my mother had called me aside, "Terry, if you would like to take Nancy to dinner in Vancouver, I've saved twenty-five dollars."

"Really, mother? Sounds great! We'll take you up — thanks lots and lots!"

To get to the restaurant, we had to ride a special cable bus almost straight up the side of the mountain. The sun was still up as we stepped into the hanging car for our ascent. The sky did have a few clouds, which only served to spread out the evening sun's beams as though they were falling from some just-opened shutters in the heavens.

We looked down from the ascending car, and Nancy sort of kiddingly said, "Terry, what if this thing falls?"

"We'd all be killed!" I replied with half a grin.

Nancy grinned, too, "Ya' think so?" We laughed about it together. I guess had we realized the seriousness of the issue, we wouldn't have taken the thought so lightly, but death was about as remote as going to Antarctica for the rest of our lives.

"Monsieur, I am sorry to inform the gentleman that we are out of shrimp. Would Monsieur care for crab?" the French waiter told us at the top after we had placed our order.

"Uh, the lady will take the crab, uh-et pour Monsieur — uh, avez vous les escarots?"

"Oui, Monsieur, c'est bon!"

"L'escarots pour moi — uh — s'il vous plait!" I requested, as Nancy beamed from across the table at this display of French. It was not really that good, but impressive to anyone who was foreign to it. I didn't tell her that I didn't know what "escarots" meant.

Then they brought us our appetizers — Nancy the crab, and me the snails. Not bad, dipped in butter.

"Let's talk a little about our honeymoon, sweetheart," I suggested.

"Oh, I'm looking forward to it so much," Nancy replied.

"We have several choices."

"The mountains would be so pretty."

"How about leaves at that time of year?"

"I guess we'll have to look into it."

"I've thought about the tropics."

"You mean Florida?"

"Yes, Florida or Nassau or the Bahamas — I sort of like it down there."

"Yes, and there's Jekyll Island. I've heard so much about it."

"Or we could go to upstate New York and Niagara and all."

"Oh, Terry, I just know it's going to be perfect."

"I suppose that anywhere we happen to be will seem ideal."

"And the wedding, Terry," Nancy went on, as the lights of the city glistened a little more brightly. "We must decide on how many we are going to have in it."

"I just can't think," I replied, "but I know we can't have twelve of each."

And our enchanted evening continued in the elegant and foreign atmosphere.

All too quickly our six weeks had flown by, but in just ten more, we would be married and once-and-for-all together, never to be separated again. We had had enough separation — no more for us — nothing or no one would be able to pry us apart again. But ten weeks was still a long time, and each of the seventy days would drag by like a lifetime.

One last surprise still awaited us, however. Several of my aunts had gathered the whole clan of relatives together under the guise of a picnic. But they surprised us with a shower of multitudes of rich gifts for our future home. We could hardly believe our eyes when they sat us down and began carting out gorgeously wrapped packages.

"Oh, y'all, this is just so nice of you — I just can't believe it," Nancy exclaimed from her heart.

Days had been too short for us in the Evergreen State, and the hour came to say good-bye.

"Mrs. Thomas, I just don't know how to say thank you for all you've been and done since I've been here."

"Nancy, we are just real proud of you and Terry and so happy that he is getting *you* for his wife."

"Tell your folks hello for us," dad told her. "We'll be there in November." And we were all smiling good-byes from ear to ear as I headed the car towards the Seattle-Tacoma airport. Nancy and I were sad in parting, but happy in knowing we would soon be together again.

Nancy kept saying, "Terry, I just don't want to leave — I want to stay — in fact, I think I might!"

12 Preparations

For the next several weeks our relationship went through one of its most difficult times. We found ourselves engrossed in plans for the wedding and new home, while terribly caught up with anticipation that nearly burst our hearts.

Things in Atlanta began on a fresh, clear note when Nancy returned. Her first letter included:

> Mother started talking about the wedding almost as soon as I got off the plane — she's *real* excited, *so* is daddy — momma has so many good and original ideas about flowers, etc.

It is amazing how many little things are involved in wedding preparations. One that drew more than a nod of attention from me had to do with one of those secret surprises a bride has for her new husband once they are married. Nancy hinted:

> Sure have gotten some pretty things, too — but I'll surprise you on November 24th (about 12 P.M.). That was sort of a big hint, wasn't it?

One big problem we had was who and how many attendants to have in the ceremony.

> Ter, all these girls are close to me. All need to be in it. But twelve attendants — that would look like a three-ring service or else like a coronation ceremony. Now, what can I do? Help — please.

We had quite a time getting this problem worked out through our letters, but finally decided on nine — nine bridesmaids and nine groomsmen.

I guess no matter how big the wedding, if it's to be organized and planned, it's got to be more than fun — headaches, worries, frustrations, and money.

Soon the time came to get started on some of the personal matters. Nancy and I knew we didn't want children right away, but, of course, wanted to start a family before too long.

> I hate to mention this in a letter, but I want to know what you think before my doctor appointment, if possible. Do you think it's all right for me to take pills? I have to start on them soon, and when I go to the doctor he will probably tell me about them. I want to be sure that there are no harmful aftereffects to the children. Otherwise, I see no reason not to take them.

She did start on the pills, and those little miracle gems weren't particularly easy for my wife-to-be to get accustomed to; in fact, for a few days they caused some difficulties, and a few weeks later she wrote:

> I've been feeling kind of "cryee" lately — think it's the pills. Really let loose today.

In the midst of all these preparations, we still found a few moments to think about some of the details we'd confront after the wedding. Nancy reminded:

> When you come, please bring me the bedroom window measurements and a sample of the bedspread (a thread from underneath or something).

I cannot say how eagerly we awaited moving into our apartment together. Nancy wrote how one night the tears of excitement just had to come out — she couldn't contain herself or her feelings. I wrote back:

> I'll tell you, I understand your crying. I feel that way myself. You feel so good inside — yet, it isn't quite here — so you just about break wide open. The closer it gets, the more you anticipate it, and you just can hardly stand it.

So we were sometimes driven beyond endurance with inner excitement. September 24th, Nancy wrote:

> Only two months from tonight and I will be Mrs. Terry Thomas. How about that? Think you can get used to it?

I surely did!!! Man, it sounded sweet!

There was something so wonderful in store for us, that, indeed, such ecstasy entering our lives was an impossible dream. Nancy revealed her secret heart — her will, motivation, and desire — even more as late one night she thoughtfully penned:

My darling,   2:00 A.M.

I've been lying in bed thinking about you and praying that God will make me the kind of wife you need, that He will make me more willing to please than be pleased, that He will teach me not to pursue happiness selfishly, for happiness comes when you forget self, that He will make us both realize in our hearts as well as in our heads what "for better or for worse, sickness and health," etc., means. But, most of all, that He will mold us together as one, that through our marriage and because of it we will grow in loving — love to each other and to others as the years go by — and even more than that — because of our life together, we will grow closer to our Lord.

These things would all be wild dreams without trust in the Lord. For it hit me tonight that without *Him* none of them are possible. It hit me because, being human, this is not my nature.

With Jesus we can have a harmony in our marriage that this world knows nothing about. How I love you and how it scares me that sometime I may fail to show you. I ask God daily to make me more loving and to make me open in sharing it.

I don't know if I have ever told you this, but your love — which I always see, which is always gentle — has been a great inspiration.

I want you so much — just to look at you and talk to you. I am more and more thankful every day that the Lord has shown us to marry in November. I want to start life with you — a new life — *right now.*

While she was in Atlanta carrying the load of the wedding plans, I was in Philadelphia planning the honeymoon, and with the travel agent, I began making reservations I knew we'd both enjoy. I wanted something especially unusual to surprise my new bride. The plan was for a grand honeymoon in the Bahamas. When I wrote Nancy the full and complete surprise, she excitedly replied:

The hotel for the honeymoon looks *out of this world.* (I had included brochures of the hotels we would be in.)

I won't even ask you how all this is possible. You certainly are a neat honeymoon planner — too bad everyone isn't getting a husband like you. *Our* honeymoon would be unique no matter where we went, but this is *far more* than I dreamed of. I'm glad you have champagne tastes. That suits me fine.

Meanwhile, Nancy was snowed over with last minute details, showers, and parties.

For the next month there are seven parties — about two a week, which will be fun. I sure don't deserve them. Don't know why people are so sweet to us.

I even got to pop into one of those honorable occasions — or should I say I got "pushed"? About two weeks before the wedding, I flew down to Atlanta for the weekend, and on Saturday Nancy was being given one of her luncheon parties. The girls thought it would be so nice if they could meet me, and hoped I could drop in for a few minutes. Of course, Nancy said I didn't have to, but when did I turn down a challenge?

Nancy's brother Tommy came along as backup man, and somehow we did shuffle our way through. Really, it went very well; only the forethought was painful.

As the wedding day closed in upon us, other details began to fall into place, too — for example, gifts. Nancy was so delighted when the first one came.

Guess what? We got our first wedding present today. Oh, darling, I wish you could be here to open them. Maybe I'll save the rest of them, except we'd have to write "thank you" notes for the next six months.

Finally, the week zoomed in, and with dozens of lives and thousands of miles to travel involved, I wrote in one of my letters:

One week from today and the numbness of anticipation will be shocked out of place.
Tomorrow the family gets in — have a lot of work to do to get ready — time will fly.

My family was due at Philadelphia International on Saturday evening, November 18th, one week before the wedding, and I had done my best to make proper preparations. We would spend a couple of days together and then go on as a family to Georgia. I had moved up to Pennsylvania from Washington, D.C., that fall, so Nancy and I looked forward to having our first home there. I had rented a choice new apartment which I felt we both would like.

The family did arrive, and for the next two days we packed in as much sightseeing as possible; Independence Square, Valley Forge, and all of Washington, D.C. kept us busy.

We even included a visit with our congressman, and hearing Bobby Kennedy give a speech in the Senate Chamber was a special thrill. Then on Tuesday morning, we left for Decatur, Georgia.

The Groovers and Thomases had never met. Among other preparations, Nancy had had the whole family outside on Saturdays painting the trim on the house, shearing shrubbery, raking leaves, and numerous other chores.

The Thomas family had been trying on clothes, buying new outfits, and getting their hair done that they, too, might present that "just so" look.

We boarded the plane in Philadelphia early that November morning, and an hour and a half later swooped down for our landing at the Atlanta International. My proud bride was anxiously waiting on the concourse with her parents when we deplaned.

"I know you're Cliff," Jane said with a wide grin for dad the moment we stepped off, before we could even begin introductions.

"And Norma!" Sol said with a gigantically wide smile.

"Here are the twins," Jane said. "Now which is which?"

"Sol, it's good to meet you folks," I heard dad jovially say as we all broke out in various conversations at the same time.

I overheard mother, "Oh, it took just an hour and a half."

Everyone seemed to be getting along so well that Nancy and I quickly slipped off to fetch the car. And in the privacy of the parking lot, our eyes met in a quiet, silent way that seemed to say, *"Never again — no — no more partings — no more good-byes — finally, my sweetheart, to be together at last and forever."* The solitude and oblivion of the moment was especially meaningful, for before too long we had to start the car and continue the busy festivities of the week.

Dinner at the Groover's, after we had checked into our motel, was delicious, and it was a good time for everyone to get acquainted. Before long, though, Nancy got me alone and told me some things that nearly made her cry.

"Oh, Terry, just everything has gone wrong. I have some terrible news."

"Won't they give us our license?" I said with a laugh. But she didn't laugh with me.

"Terry, your blood test is out of date and you've got to do it again." She knew how I hated to have a needle poked in to draw blood.

"Ow," I blurted out.

"And that's not all," she said. "Then we have to take it over to the courthouse for the license."

"What's wrong with them down there?" I said. "Can't they do things right?" That was the wrong thing to say, for there was more. I guess we both were tense.

"Tommy'll take you so you won't have to worry about getting lost or anything," she assured me.

"I hate that needle!" I said, adding to her troubled thoughts.

"You know the rings?"

"Didn't you pick them up?" I asked. We had left them at the engravers, and she was to have picked them up two weeks ago.

"No, they didn't have them done!"

"They didn't what?"

"Terry, they haven't finished them, and we can't pick them up 'til tomorrow."

"Well, at least there couldn't be anything else," I told her, trying to be gentle.

"Oh, I hate to think of this, but mama's new coat didn't come either."

"Well, let's check on it."

"It's already too late, and she bought another one today," I was assured, but from a voice heavily burdened. "Oh, Terry, I hate to tell you all this — but the worst is yet to come."

"What could be worse — more blood — sitting in the courthouse — pushing the jewelry store — no clothes?" In retrospect, this all sounds quite minor, but at the time with all the other pressures, it seemed awful big.

"Terry, my new negligee is lost," and she nearly broke into

tears. True to tradition, the details of the garment were not disclosed to me, but I found out later that she had spent days with her mother and girlfriends looking in stores for a perfect negligee to please her husband on their first night together. They finally found and purchased the ideal, the only one in town she liked — and she was thrilled with it. But when they got home, it wasn't in her bag.

"Terry, I called the store and it isn't there — they've searched all over for it."

"Then it has to be in the car or in your bag — or maybe you lost it on the way from the store to the car."

"No, because mama was with me! Terry, I just don't know what to do."

But much to her relief — not mine so much, except that it mattered to her — it was found. Somehow, it had slipped under a wheel of the car in the garage and was discovered undamaged, but not until after abrasing that tender, soft heart of Nancy's.

The blood test, the license, the rings, and all the details worked out just fine, too, as Tommy and I hopped from one place to another on the following day.

The Groover household was bustling with activity all day and beginning to bulge as the countdown began and zero hour loomed in upon us.

Countdown? Zero hour? Planned details? Pressure? Did our Lord want all this? If we were late for one of our planned activities, we'd be tense. Solution? Not being on time — that's self-satisfaction, not Christ satisfaction. What about not having detailed plans?

Out-of-town guests began arriving for the preliminaries preceding the main event. Dad and I latched onto a rent-a-car while Nancy, her mother, and the ladies from my family joined the bridesmaids for a special luncheon, and somehow the day just flew by, leaving the calendar with only two days to go.

When Sol had a chance, he took me aside for some special last minute instructions.

"Now, Terry, we'll have Nancy at the church on time. You be there at 6:30!" I thought for a minute he might be kidding, for it never occurred to me that I might be late. But then I knew better, because he had been familiar with weddings where the bride or the groom had skipped out at the last minute, leaving the other standing at the altar.

In the evening, as the folks were enjoying each other's company, Nancy and I drove over to the motel where we could decelerate a bit and watch television.

"Terry, do you think we'll make it?" Nancy uttered as we relaxed together.

"Make what, honey?"

"Oh, just getting through all this!"

"Do you want to just take our license and get married tonight?" I casually suggested.

"We could."

"Ya, I know it."

"Remember when we had 125 days to go?"

"It seemed like it would never get there — still doesn't."

"Will it ever come?"

We prayed together before I took her home, and I noticed she was beginning to show signs of wear. I insisted she sleep in the next morning, which she did, for Thursday — Thanksgiving — would be an even bigger day.

It began for me about quarter to nine when the phone rang.

13 Remember When

It was Irwin, the best man, my cousin from Chicago. He had driven all night and was on the outskirts of town.

"Hey, old man, what in the world you doin', you horse thief?" I hollered over the phone.

"Oh, Terry," I heard mother say.

"Well, I thought I better come down and make sure my low-down, good-for-nothin' cousin didn't back out of this thing."

"How do I get out there?" he asked, and I relayed the directions.

By the time Irwin arrived, we were ready for breakfast. And in the restaurant I was paged, as we were eating our eggs and grits, for a phone call from my brother-in-law. He was at the airport, having just flown in from Seattle. I dispatched my dad and sister (his wife) to the terminal to pick him up.

After eating, Irwin and I took his Barracuda over to Nancy's where the house was as busy as ever. Nancy was under the hair dryer, but that didn't matter. We knew that the next day we wouldn't see each other at all until the wedding, so wanted to make the most of it. Several bridesmaids were there, too, but we at least got to stare.

After a few minutes, we took Tommy and drove around trying to find a car wash to clean the Barracuda. Only Irwin and I knew, but far in advance we had planned to use his car for the getaway.

Meanwhile, out-of-towners were arriving rapidly. The first was one of the groomsmen and his fiancée from Washington, D. C.

Not far behind them another carload pulled in from the same area. Later, Dave Field, my good friend with whom I had shared so closely during the summer, drove in, from Dallas.

Our motel was about half full of folks who had come just for the wedding. It was rather amusing to us that when stepping out of our room that afternoon we noticed some folks just going into theirs. They looked at us, too, but no one said anything. They watched us walk out of the corner of their eyes as we glanced at them. Then, almost at the same time, we said, "Ah —" and a little chuckle. Then, carefully, "Are you here for the wedding?"

And a big "Yes!"

"We're from south of here," they said.

"Oh, so good to meet you — I'm the groom!"

"Oh, you are? We know all about you, Terry; we're so glad to finally meet you — c'mon in!"

Finally evening came and time for rehearsal, which was to be followed by a rehearsal dinner. Irwin and I picked up Nancy and arrived at the church a little late, hoping everyone would already be there. The three of us walked in quietly and confidently — sort of like stars. I learned something about women — well, men, too — that night, that I never knew before.

Being as close as Nancy and I had grown, we never kept a secret from the other. In our exchanges we had discovered that the single men and women in the wedding party previous to coming had asked us individually, as their close friends, about the other guys or the gals, as the case might be, and we could tell that each had interests in this one or that.

So, I fully expected when we entered the church to find the men and women mingling and at least showing a willingness to get acquainted. But what a surprise to see a cluster of men in one corner, joking and laughing, and a cluster of women in another corner completely ignoring them. And as the rehearsal began the great interest they had spoken in confidence was completely covered by nonchalance. I guess love is, at times, a bit of a game.

Soon the organist began pressing the keys that released the tones for the rehearsal of the bridal march. The men and women were lined up according to heights and both ministers stood in place. I was pushed around a little from side to side, too, in an attempt to align for greater effect, but still wasn't sure where to stand or when and where I was to move. Numbness began to set in.

Finally, down the aisle came the bride — rather her stand-in, my cousin.

The bride herself was not allowed in the rehearsal due to tradition; I don't know why the groom was.

So, down the aisle came Cousin Sandie, while Nancy looked on.

"Who gives this bride to this man?" I heard Dr. Phillips say as Sandie stood beside me. I felt a pang of fright pierce my side. Then they came to the part where I was supposed to say my vows from memory, and I couldn't think of them.

"I Terry — uh — take thee Nancy to be my wife — I mean, wedded wife. I guess I'd better learn this for tomorrow," I said; feeling indignant stares from all around.

And then we began once again for a final run-through. Each chord of the "Bridal March" hit a note of something between sentimentality and fear. And it was especially long in this wedding, for nine bridesmaids had to slowly make their way from the rear to the front and take their places. Things stumbled along, and even when we concluded, it didn't look like it would ever shape up for a smooth running performance on opening night.

For a moment I remembered a musical I had had the lead in in college. We rehearsed each line — each move — and then performed for an audience. I felt a little the same here. Did our Lord want a systematized performance?

After the rehearsal, forty of us made our way to the chandelier-lit dining room at the Ramada Inn for the rehearsal dinner.

"Nancy, honey, just think, eight months ago we only dreamed of this coming true," I mentioned as we sat in the middle of the head table with our parents on either side.

"I know; you just can't imagine how all of this happened when you think back."

"Those times at Daytona and finally our date and day together . . ."

I reached down and squeezed her hand.

"And then when we first began to write — we hoped we would be able to get married but didn't know for sure."

"And then how we knew for sure but not when — boy, a lot has happened!"

And then came the time for speeches. Maybe we shouldn't have opened it up to the floor, for some of the things in our "remember when" session could have been a bit embarrassing.

At my sister's wedding years earlier, I had pulled a few pranks on my brother-in-law, and he eventually made it to his feet to say with a grin, "I've come here all the way from Washington for one purpose: to even the score."

A close friend of Nancy's family rose to his feet and said, "Remember when Nancy was seven or eight how she would play the piano with her big toes — it didn't sound too bad, either." And the laughter became hilarious as story after story that we hadn't known about the other came to light.

But before the evening ended, it turned to a serious note. Nancy rose, looked calmly at the group, and began an extemporaneous speech that was, perhaps, the finest, most sincere, and best expressed she had ever given. The room silenced to a hush. Every eye turned her way.

"I am getting something beyond what I ever dreamed possible," she began, eyes brilliantly sparkling, a partial but serious smile across her lips, "and my dreams, ideals and goals have always been very high. I can't remember when I began to think about marriage, or even when I began to plan my wedding, but it was when I was a little girl." She radiated with every word as she confidently shared what was in her heart.

"The man I'm getting for a husband is beyond what I thought was ever possible. And what I've wanted to say is, that everything I have I attribute as gifts from Jesus Christ. He has been very good to me — speaking for myself — and good to us — Terry and me. Everything we have is from Him and I wanted every one of you to know that.

"And so many of you mean so much to me; I am so honored that you are here.

"We have prayed that the rest of our lives, no matter how

long, will glorify Him in some way. And we know that the love between us — as it is seen — will reveal a little part of that great love He has. I just wanted you all to know that we attribute everything we have — and we feel it is a lot — way more than we deserve or ever imagined possible — to Him."

I stood next and continued along the vein Nancy had begun. "We accept each other and our marriage as from Him. You know this, but we want to express it openly on this momentous occasion.

"We have found a deeper source of joy and peace than in just each other — it is our personal relationship with Jesus Christ. God has used us in each other's lives to bring countless joy, but again, the inner satisfaction has originated in Him alone.

"Oh, yes, we're human — get tense, frustrated, and find it easy to worry. But our Shepherd always uses His 'rod or staff' to comfort us and lead us on through these trepidations.

"And this began when we truly opened our lives up to Christ — and, of course, we wouldn't want any of our friends and loved ones to miss out on this relationship with Him.

"We want you to know that we place ourselves and what's ahead for us totally and completely into His hands.

"And I also want everyone to know that my bride is the most fabulous woman ever born on this earth. And I thank God for making her what she is, and then for giving her to me." As I sat down, it seemed as though the power of love and God were there. Soon we began rising from our tables and freely mingling and chatting.

As soon as I could, I took Nancy home. There were some people at the house, but I took her right up to her bedroom. She was totally exhausted, and so was I. I didn't want a collapsed bride at the altar the next evening, nor an ill wife on our honeymoon, so I asked her to go right to bed.

"What about the people downstairs?"

"They'll understand, and right now you are more important."

"Yes, sweetheart, I guess you're right. Terry, will tomorrow night ever come?" We started to unwind — slow down a little.

"All I know is I sure will miss you all day."

"Oh, me too. I love you so much," she slowly whispered.

"I know — and I love you — I love you even more — if that's possible."

We lingered for a few moments looking each other directly in the eyes. I could hardly keep from shivering with emotion.

Finally — "Well, my love —" and with a powerful big squeeze — "I'll see you tomorrow night in the church. Oh, how will I recognize you, having never seen the dress?"

"Ha, ha," she grinned.

"Just think, honey, the next time I see you, you will be coming down the aisle."

"And then Nassau — and Terry, then our own apartment — oh, I can hardly believe it's true."

I closed her door behind me and drove right back to the motel and went to bed.

14 Here Comes the Bride

Rather than overburden ourselves with baggage at the church, Nancy and I had decided to check into the hotel the afternoon before the wedding with most of what we were taking. I wasn't allowed to see her, of course, so Irwin drove over to her house to pick up her luggage. When he returned, we cautiously headed both cars down the freeway to the Marriot Hotel, realizing that should we be seen, suspicion would be aroused.

Pulling up to the Marriot, I slipped the doorman a tip, and he directed us to a secretive place to hide the VW. It was a dark service basement, and we buried the car in a far corner behind a pillar and chunks of plywood and two-by-fours. Back at the main entrance, unloading what Irwin had picked up from Nancy, I soon realized the baggage was tripling or quadrupling. We had everything from a hair dryer to clothes bags, and lots of suitcases. I had never realized how many things girls have to take along on a trip.

"Mr. and Mrs. T. C. Thomas checking in, please," I told the desk clerk in registering.

"Oh, yes, your room is ready. Here is your key, and if you need anything, let us know." The bellhop pushed the overloaded caddy to the elevator and up to the eleventh floor room.

"This is neat, Terry!" Irwin enthusiastically remarked as we walked through the door of the exquisite bridal suite.

"And look here, Irwin, a separate living room — and bedroom."

"Ya, you've made a good choice!"

"I wonder what we can do to make it extra special for Nancy?"

"They always like flowers!"

"That's it — a dozen roses!"

We checked the room pretty carefully, adjusted the stereo to a soothing channel and medium-low volume, and then called service.

"Could you have a dozen of the best red roses available sent up to 1121 — yes, long stemmed — and is there anything else you would suggest? Oh, that sounds real good — sure — even if they have to work overtime, do it right — yes, the very best you have — yes — and thank you!"

After one more look around and readjusting the drapes, we left. My family had agreed to eat our last dinner together at four-thirty. I glanced at my watch as we cruised back on the freeway to Decatur — four-thirty. Behind schedule.

The day was not turning out at all like I had imagined. I had expected to rise late and casually relax through the day — partially at a health spa with saunas, whirlpool baths, and a massage — and partially just taking it easy. So far, the day had been tension-filled with run, run, run, and now the magic hour of six-thirty, when we were to be at the church, was quickly approaching. And I had not had dinner, nor even a bath.

The family was waiting when Irwin and I returned. We picked them up and started towards the restaurant. Torrents of rain were pouring and thunder and lightning flashing overhead. "For the first time in forty years," the radio report said, "we have a tornado watch in Atlanta. First one in forty years — keep your eyes on the sky, and should you see a black funnel emerge — quickly. . . ." and the report went on instructing listeners what to do. A fine fall afternoon to precede our long-awaited wedding! Nancy had to walk outside in her long dress to get to the church — it couldn't rain.

After dinner we returned to the motel for final preparations and then headed for the Decatur Presbyterian Church.

Outside the church, Irwin and I tried desperately to hide the getaway vehicle. We had just found an ideal vacant lot when I noticed a tan VW with head visors down not fifty feet away.

"Irwin, flash the lights on that thing," I said. Two heads quickly bobbed down. "Pull up alongside!" Sure enough, there sat Tommy and Rob. Apparently they had followed us with their lights out, and had we parked there, it would have been sure death for the Barracuda. So, without further question or pondering, we took one of the biggest chances ever. We pulled right up to the front door of the church and parked the car, hoping it would stand out so obviously that the pranksters would believe it to be only a decoy and leave it alone.

Sol was just slipping on his trousers as I stepped into the men's dressing room. "Well, you did make it," he said.

"Yep, wouldn't miss it," I quipped with a nervous laugh. I looked at my watch. It was exactly six-thirty — right on time.

The ushers and groomsmen were joking around while getting into their black tuxedos and ties, and I passed out the jewelry cases I had brought for them as gifts.

Then, all at once, I remembered something terrible. "Irwin, my suit — for going away — I packed it in my suitcase we took to the hotel."

"Let's see," he said cooly glancing at his watch, "it's quarter to seven now, twenty minutes each way plus five minutes to run up to the room — "

"It's too close — Irwin — if something went wrong — "

"You're right. Let's see? You're six foot?" he said, sizing me up. "Ya."

"Okay, you'll wear my suit!"

"What'll you wear?"

"I'll keep the tux on."

"Okay! Sounds good."

About that time someone came in asking, "Where's Terry?"

"In here," someone else replied.

"Keep him there — a special girl's coming through he can't see."

They were bringing Nancy through the downpour outside and in the back way, for the rear entrance was closer. I was told later they used five big umbrellas. Things were moving quickly along. It was now five to seven.

A few minutes later an official looking lady brought in a box of boutonnieres and asked, "Now, where are all the men?"

"I think some are out front ready to begin," Irwin replied.

"I guess I'll have to put their boutonnieres on out there."

"What about ours?" I asked.

"I'll be back before it starts to put on yours and make sure it's done right!" With her assurance, we completely forgot about the flowers, confident they would be properly remembered.

I noticed that dad looked exceptionally sharp in his black tux as he fastened the final stud. I think he was a little nervous for me, but did not show it — he only had a funny, unexplainable pain inside that he had never felt before. "I'll make it," he assured me.

"Well, I don't know when I'll see you again," I said, as the thought ran briefly through my mind between pulses of anticipation.

"I hadn't thought of that either," was his reply. Then he had to slip out, for the magic moment was upon us.

Left behind in the stillness of the room were just two of us — Irwin and I.

It's a good thing our Lord didn't try to come to the wedding. We were all so busy with our plans and tension that He would have had to wait in a corner unrecognized. Of course, we'd bring Him out during the performance to say the part we had written for Him.

"Irwin, I need some air," I said with a bolt for the door. He was right behind. After a few puffs of the clear, wholesome stuff, we stepped back inside. I slipped into the narrow hall and took a peek into the sanctuary. It was filling up, and I could hear the soft, flowing chords from the organ begin. My heart skipped a beat, but quickly made up for it as my pulse rate rapidly increased.

I staggered back into the dressing room and could not seem to catch my breath. Irwin saw what was happening.

"Okay, Terry, now we're going to do some exercises — first, we'll touch our toes — Okay? Together — all the way down."

"Irwin, my shirt's coming out."

"Doesn't matter, we'll fix that later."

"All right."

"Okay — touch the toes — again — again — again — again — getting loose? Again — feel better? Again, all the way — again. Now, we'll loosen up our mid-muscles — swivel — together."

I didn't know if this was helping or not, but at least it took my mind off what was ahead.

"Irwin, I've got to get some more air," and leaped for the back door again. No, I had no inclination to walk out, though I suppose almost every groom would like to escape from the pressure for a minute or two.

We came back into the room just as the organist struck a resounding, ringing chord. A pang of numbness bit my face and suddenly my head felt giddy. My legs felt weak, too — and, again, the breathless sensation enveloped. Then someone knocked on the door. "Men, be ready in two minutes!" I jumped to my feet as though I had been sitting on a tack which was not felt until just then.

Hurriedly, I began stuffing my shirt into my trousers as I ran to the rest room for one last check in the mirror. On the way back to the sanctuary, I noticed I had no pulse — it had speeded beyond the point of counting. They began opening the door ahead of us — I was in front, Irwin backing me up, when panic struck.

"Irwin, our flowers!"

"Oh, my goodness," he said and ran back to the dressing room. There had been a slip-up and our boutonnieres had not been placed on our lapels. Irwin tore back with them — special little pink roses — and two pins. We quickly fumbled around and stuck them in place. The door opened and we marched front and center to where eight men were already waiting. As I looked up and saw the serious-faced guests, I never came closer to fainting in all my life. And I dared not move. My position had been blocked out for me. Somehow, I kept myself from succumbing by looking to the rear. Colors were non-existent — everything was blurry and in black and white.

Then the music stopped for just an instant, but quickly began again — this time precisely and carefully to the "Bridal March."

Slowly and cautiously the first young lady of the court began the long trip down the aisle. She was, perhaps, the cutest of the nine — Nancy's ten-year-old sister, Mary. She looked as precious as a little doll — the kind you wanted to pick up and squeeze.

The wedding had begun. Nothing could stop it now. Then

behind Mary methodically marched another. Slowly! And another — she seemed slower yet.

The girls were pretty in their red dresses and veils. They all looked proud to be a part. They kept coming. Where was Nancy? I had lost count. Had fifteen gone by? No, there were only nine altogether!

There was a pause in the processional. The music softened.

Then, with sudden crescendo and added stops — strings and sixteen foot and two couplers — the "Bridal March" filled the sanctuary from its high roof to its fully prepared surface below — causing every guest to turn his head to the rear of the sanctuary. I saw the gray-haired gentleman who would soon be my father-in-law. He stood there, handsome as a king — a real gentleman — proud and stately in his black tuxedo. Then I saw a patch of white — then an arm — then moving into the doorway and standing in place — Nancy — my bride. Finally! The aisle was long and Nancy stood what seemed miles away, but I felt a confident, loving, heart tucked deep inside the beautiful girl ready to reveal itself in totality to me waiting in front.

Her hand rested on her father's arm as they slowly started toward the front. Broadly, with feeling, the music continued and the emotion of the moment filled the sanctuary. For months Nancy and I had talked about this moment, wondering what it would be like, and suddenly it was here. Nothing could slow it down, speed it up, or change it.

A clear smile was on Nancy's face as she and her father proceeded. She was absolutely gorgeous. She looked at me — I watched only her. Her father helped her make the turn at the front, and then they calmly came and stood beside me — Mr. Groover between us.

I could see she was excited. Then five of us — the matron of honor, Nancy's father, Nancy, Irwin and I — came to a quiet, serious stance and turned to face the ministers. The organ music heralding the coming of the bride had faded into a pianissimo and then terminated. Dr. Phillips broke the silence as the entire congregation sat forward to listen.

"Dearly beloved, we are assembled here in the presence of God and these witnesses to unite Terry Clifford Thomas and

Nancy Jane Groover in the bonds of holy marriage. Marriage is a gift of God, our Father, and tonight we receive this covenant as from Him.

"The Scripture says, 'And we know that God causes all things to work together for good to those who love God, to those who are called according to His purpose.' And, 'For everything created by God is good, and nothing is to be rejected, if it is received with gratitude.' The charge in marriage is spoken by the Apostle Paul, 'And be kind to one another, tender-hearted, forgiving each other just as God in Christ also has forgiven you.'"

The guests were still and quiet.

"Our Lord Jesus Christ held marriage in the highest esteem as He said, 'For this cause a man shall leave his father and mother, and shall cleave to his wife; and the two shall become one flesh.'

"Let us pray: God, our Father, let Thy Son, Jesus Christ, be lifted up tonight in this service and throughout Nancy's and Terry's marriage. We thank Thee that Thy love for us has no bounds, and that You will never forsake us."

Nancy and I had painstakingly written our own ceremony, with thoughts and words we felt best suited us on this occasion — some words from others — some of our own. As Dr. Phillips read on, my mind wandered a moment and I glanced sideways at my bride. She glanced at me, too, and I knew that her attention had left the ceremony as had mine. We spoke to each other in our private, wordless language. I noticed her pink rose bouquet and could almost see the pretty hands which it covered. Meanwhile, Dr. Phillips was proceeding.

"Who gives this woman to be married to this man?" Confidently and clearly, as though each word was extremely important, Mr. Groover said his part:

"Her mother and I."

Suddenly, as we glanced at each other, I felt a tremendous calmness I had not felt previously that day. We seemed to melt together, forgetting anyone else was even near. I could not dream of the honeymoon; she could not dream of the apartment which was fully prepared. This moment was sufficient. She was beautiful beyond words.

Then the memorized part which had begun to mean so much, when I was to speak, came. I turned to Nancy and began, She looked straight into my eyes.

"I, Terry, take thee, Nancy, to be my wedded wife. . . ."

"I, Nancy," she spoke so beautifully with confidence and softly with deep meaning, "take thee, Terry, to be my wedded husband, to live together under God's guidance in spiritual fellowship of marriage. I will love, honor, cherish," and this is where the most beautiful surprise of my entire life came in. I knew her vows from memory as she knew mine. I expected the next word "thee" to follow, but she inserted a different one — one I had not written — one that thrilled me. A depth-filled glow crossed her face and she said the words, "and *obey* thee." I could not believe my ears. Such fabulous submission, and I knew she meant it. Without pause she continued, noticing the surprised smile that had struck me — and that thrilled her.

"In sickness as in health, in poverty as in wealth, in sorrow as in joy, and be true to thee, and by God's grace trust Him, so long as we both shall live."

Rev. Wilson then asked:

"Terry, what token do you give in recognition of this pledge?"

We exchanged rings and Dr. Phillips concluded:

"For as much as you, Nancy, and you, Terry, have consented to holy wedlock and pledged your undying devotion to each other, I now pronounce you husband and wife. What God has joined together, let no man put asunder."

We started down the steps and made our way up the aisle trying not to look like we were in a hurry. At the end of the aisle, I kissed Nancy and we kissed again — and once more.

Photos, slicing the cake, receiving of guests, all went smoothly. But in the back of my mind, I knew we would have to evade the pranksters before making it to our hotel. And we knew they would not give up easily.

We also knew Nancy's ten-year-old sister, Mary, would not be able to keep a secret, so during the reception Irwin called her aside. "Mary, I like you very much and I want you to keep a secret. This will be just between you and me."

"Oh, I won't tell anybody."

"Mary, Nancy and Terry are going to Stone Mountain tonight — now, don't tell Tom or Rob." In a few minutes we noticed that Mary made her way to her older brother, Rob.

The reception line seemed to pass quickly and soon the reception was drawing to a close. After another piece of cake and a glass of punch, I walked Nancy to her dressing room, but was afraid to let her out of sight. So I placed Irwin at the door and took another trusted friend, Randy, with me.

Randy and I talked some as I quickly changed into Irwin's suit. Hurriedly I slipped back to Irwin guarding Nancy's dressing room. Nancy was ready and her folks were inside. I called my parents in and we all kissed and said our last good-byes. It was especially difficult for Nancy's family, for their daughter was the oldest child and had meant so much to them at home. Yet they were extremely happy that their wish for Nancy, a wonderful marriage, was being fulfilled. And, of course, they would see her soon again — at Christmas.

"Good-bye, mama, and you, too, daddy." They almost began to cry a little.

"Son, God bless you," dad said, and that was enough.

"Nancy, as I told you, the apartment should be ready — and the drawer in the kitchen we filled with canned goods — and we love you so much," my mother added.

"Okay, dad, you tell Irwin to start the car, and when it's running, open the door and tell me."

"What's that, now?" he asked nervously, having a little difficulty keeping it all straight. Soon he peeked in from the hall and said, "It's all set." The Barracuda was running untouched.

"Okay — let's go."

"GOOD-BYE" — "GOOD-BYE" — "Good-bye" — "Good-bye" —"good-bye" — "good-bye" —

Hand in hand, we tore down the hall through a storm of rice to the outside — where we ran into some shrubbery. Quickly recovering our balance, we made it to the car. Irwin was revving up the engine as I tore open the door. I threw in Nancy's little suitcase and began to put her in the back seat.

"Terry — oo — Terry," she screamed. I pulled a little harder, intent on getting her in, and then looked around to see that one of my men, Al, was holding her other arm. Without even thinking, I reared back and cocked my arm to full strength with clenched fist squeezed so tight I am sure it turned white, and at the last moment Al turned her loose and jumped back as his big laugh turned to surprise.

We both piled into the back seat and screeched off with a squeal.

"Oh, Nancy, we are on our way," I told her with a big hug.

Behind us trailed about a dozen determined vehicles — determined to chase us to the end. Some had their lights out.

We made the turn towards Stone Mountain and followed the speed limit explicitly. After a mile we came up behind a slow-moving car. A crashing disharmony of horns trailed through the neighborhoods we passed. Ahead we could see three cars approaching. At the last minute, Irwin and I were on the same wave length, for, as I said, "Okay — hit it," he tromped the gas to the floor and we passed the two cars just in time. The string behind us was not able to get by. Over one hill — then another — a right turn on a back road — and safe! No one was in sight. We were lost momentarily, but soon found our bearings and made our way at sensible speed back to downtown Atlanta.

Pulling into the Marriot, we took no chances.

"Irwin, if they were afraid of being thrown off our track, they may have staked out a couple of the leading hotels, so first slip in and case the lobby." Nancy and I sat anxiously in the car while Irwin was gone — what seemed like a long time. We had a laugh about Tommy's calling all the hotels in town to see if we were registered. I had instructed the Marriot to release information to no one — a charge they had kept.

Irwin returned and escorted us into the beautiful, traditionally southern hotel. The lobby looked brighter than before — more luxurious as we passed through. We said good-bye to Irwin at the elevator.

"Now you two kids hang onto that faith of yours," Irwin said in a final sentimental parting word. "You've really got something."

We were on our own. Finally alone, together, married, and

free. The eleventh floor door opened, and we stepped out of the elevator and into our room.

"Terry," Nancy exclaimed, spying the roses, "what is this?"

"Oh, just a little something for my bride."

"Terry, you're so wonderful," she cried enthusiastically as we clung to each other.

"Oh, not half as wonderful as the one I'm married to."

After a few kisses, I realized we had not closed the door. I did so and then we sat down on the couch, worn to exhaustion.

"Whew," I said, "what an ordeal. Can you believe it's over?"

"No! Oh, Terry, we're finally here."

"Everything has gone so well!" We thought just a little of the immediate future — the reservations in Fort Lauderdale and Nassau, and, of course, the apartment.

The next day we would get up late, have breakfast served in our room, and then drive south on our honeymoon. We knew we would probably get about to the Florida border and stay in a motel there. We would not hurry but take our time and enjoy the first day of marriage to the fullest.

The secret Nancy had for me was soon to be disclosed. She went into the dressing room and slipped into the beautiful, white negligee she had lost — then found. I opened my suitcase and scrambled into my new pajamas, slipped over to the stereo, and then sort of slumped down on the end of the bed.

I lowered the lights, and she opened the door to come into the room. . . .

15 The Crash

Mid-morning light was flooding our room as I opened my eyes. I looked with enchantment over at Nancy, still drowsy with sleep beside me. To ask myself if this really was true would be too trite. I was hypnotized by her very presence with me.

We were still in our robes when breakfast was served in 1121. The waiter rolled in the petite dejeuner on a small table complete with a light yellow table cloth and matching cloth napkins. It tasted more delicious than usual. More satisfying.

We almost had to pinch ourselves — was this really real?

After eating, we relaxed, being so contented and relieved to have the wedding festivities behind. Now together — forever! No more parting — no more good-byes.

It was two-thirty that afternoon before we got the VW packed and left the Marriot for our Florida and Bahama honeymoon. Nancy held in her lap the red rose bouquet I had sent up to the room for her the previous day.

We admired the luscious sunset together as we drove along, and then about six o'clock a light sprinkle began to fall. We were both really exhausted, and Nancy failed to respond in conversation — she had fallen asleep.

It began raining a little harder and grew darker. Then 6:20 — the fatal moment we had never imagined in our wildest dreams closed in. We were cruising well under control in our lane at about fifty-five miles per hour.

All at once, it came. So unexpectedly! I had never seen headlights moving in my direction so fast in all my life — now they flew out of control — now they were sliding and skidding — but in the other lane, forty feet away. I started to say, "Nancy," but all I got out was "N —." I did not even get my foot off the gas. Before I knew it, the advancing headlights jumped off the highway and flew toward us . . . then nothing anymore. . . .

I felt smothered, a horrible frightening nightmare had entombed me. I couldn't move — barely breathe — hardly see. It wouldn't seem to shake off. I was choking. Over and over, headlights kept flashing at us, striking to within six inches again and again. A ceiling — a roof was above me, and I felt like we were riding in a car — only I was still laying down. Flashing, revolving — again — again. I could hear serious talking in a muffled tone, but couldn't understand it. I felt terrible — rotten, tormented, anguished, deserted, and alone; and the headlights kept repeating their incandescent impressions upon my stricken eyes.

"Ohhhhh," my weak voice trembled. "Oh — no — no,"
Questions flashed through my mind.
"Who am I?
"Where am I?
"Am I dead? Heaven can't be like this!
"What is happening? Can someone help? Please?"
I had peered from the crushed position of the car at the scene of the crash. I had opened my eyes to see red lights flashing, torches being waved, and to sense quick tugs and efforts at freeing my body. Apparently, my frame was so pinned down that several men working frantically were needed to ease it from the wreckage. I did not move a muscle, not even a nerve. I wasn't able. I was dazed and in a stupor. My eyes were unaware of Nancy beside me, but I remember gazing for a moment at a white automobile lodged in the grassy bank nearby. All of these happenings came with such trauma that the memory was hidden deep inside my mind and not revealed until three months later.

The ambulance was streaking to the hospital. I learned later that I was receiving oxygen.
I also learned that the needle to inject a stimulant into the

blood of extremely critical cases to keep them alive had accidentally broken, and the men were frightened that I might not make it to the hospital. They had already taken me to one hospital, but it was discovered that my condition was too critical and complex for the physicians and equipment there, so we were dashing twenty-five miles further to a larger town with better facilities.

"What is going on?" I softly breathed, but so quietly no one heard. "What is going on?" with a little more effort. "What is going on?" I kept trying to find out as the interior hollowness of my being hauntingly lingered.

"There's been a bad accident," I heard an authoritative but gentle voice from somewhere outside speak.

What happened in the next few moments was to change the course of my disposition and remains crystal clear in my mind forever. Whatever occurred was terrible and harshly final. I also knew I was alone. I did not know what had gone wrong, what was going to happen, nor who was taking care of me, and I also knew I could not in the least help myself.

A thought came to my mind from out of the blank where hollow emptiness pervaded. "Lord, I don't know what has happened," I prayed in my mind as the bleakness faded a little, "I don't know who is taking care of me, but I invite You, well I guess I don't need to invite You, You are *already* taking care of me. Thank You, Lord, yes. *Right now* You are already watching over all this and Your hands are in control. You are all I have."

From that moment on a peace seemed to take hold, even though surrounded by fading hopelessness and intense pain.

"What has happened?" I tried to ask in a weak whisper. "What has happened?" I had to slowly enunciate as my voice seemed inaudible and expressionless. Then I began to see a face tower above me and could hear it whisper, though not a word was understood. They were debating, it turned out later, whether or not it would be advisable to tell all of the truth. The statement they did give, however, was the truth — at least partially.

"Where are we?" I slowly enunciated. "Where — are — we?" My memory had been momentarily jolted into amnesia.

"You've been to Adel. Now we're taking you to Tifton."

"Of course," I thought, "just a little accident and in a couple of days we'll be on our way."

We? Oh — yes, we!

"What day is it?"

"Saturday."

"What time?"

"Seven-twenty."

"What is the date?"

"The twenty-fifth."

"The twenty-fifth of what?"

"Twenty-fifth of November."

"Then it wasn't a dream — yes, just as I suspected," I continued, mumbling, "last night was Friday. We got married last night," I slowly told the men as I tried to force a little smile, beginning to remember who I was. "We have put ourselves completely into the hands of Christ."

I sensed a ruffling and whispering from somewhere.

"Yes, oh, where is Nancy?" I questioned.

No answer!

I waited a moment. "How — is — my — wife?" I demanded in a painful and breathless whisper, believing that she was all right. At the scene of the crash, I had heard someone holler the truth, but I rejected it — and forgot it. So deep in shock my heart's subconscious felt a great hollowness, but my mind overruled and let me believe that we would be together again.

"Your wife is all right," they finally told me.

"Where is she?" I slowly asked.

After a pause — "She's in Adel," the well-controlled voice assured, "and she can come up and be with you tomorrow, if you like."

"Oh, yes, we'll definitely want that," my face brightened a little, as my heart imagined a quick recovery which would soon send us south once again on our honeymoon.

I then slowly and logically deduced as the ambulance tore along. "If I'm going to Tifton because it's larger, and Nancy is in Adel and it's smaller, then she must not be hurt as bad as I am?" I saw a reaffirming nod. "And I'm all right, so Nancy is hardly hurt," I reasoned. The concern for Nancy grew as amnesia faded a little.

"You'd best save your strength," they advised as my mind visualized my side of the car getting the brunt of it and Nancy receiving just scratches. My deeper mind, however, knew better and kept me in critical shock — a violent disturbance of my mind and emotions caused by the staggering attack.

The peace I had from Christ did not pull me out of shock nor immediately heal all my injuries. But what it did do was give me an attitude of acceptance — that He had control of the situation. The ambulance continued screeching along, screaming the siren.

My mind reasoned clearly for a few more moments as an urgent thought came to mind.

"Please — please listen. Give the airport a call — page my folks and tell them what has happened. Their plane leaves at eight-thirty. They should be just about there by now." I wasn't going to rest. What for? And they didn't seem to get the message from my mumbling lips. So, after a minute, being determined to fulfill my mission, I croaked out, finding it extremely difficult and painful to breathe, "What time is it now?"

"It's seven-thirty."

"They'll be out at the airport by now! Listen! Please — carefully. Call — the — airport — and — page — my — folks — tell — them — what — has — happened. And — do — take — your — very — best — care — of — my — wife." And I fell unconscious again.

I awoke to find myself laying on a stretcher on the floor with six or eight sets of eyes blankly and emptily staring down. Someone knelt beside me.

"I'm Officer Pendleton," he said. "Is your wife's family in Decatur?"

"Yes. Did you call my folks?"

"Which airport?" he asked, having been briefed by the ambulance attendant. It never dawned on me that there was more than one airport.

"The Atlanta airport."

"And Groover is your father-in-law?"

"Yes, in Decatur."

"Where does he live?"

"On Piney Ridge, the phone is — let me think a minute — 685-4479, and please, listen very carefully." He put his ear to my mouth as I strenuously repeated, "The plane leaves at eight-thirty. They should be boarding by now." I noticed he stepped out rather quickly.

In Atlanta, the joys of newly-made friendships were at their peak as the Groovers escorted their new in-laws, the Thomases, to the airport for a happy departure.

The phone rang at the Groover's at 8 P.M. Nancy's aunt answered and could not believe her ears. She knew help was needed immediately. She summoned a neighbor, and he immediately placed a call to the airport.

"Telephone for Mr. Groover — Mr. S. M. Groover, telephone, please," the loudspeaker in the terminal blared.

"Mr. Groover, please call central control," it continued.

The wedding party was shaking hands and saying last good-byes. They were ascending the loading ramp as the final call for Flight 837 to Seattle was announced.

"Well, Cliff and Norma, we can't say how delighted we are in getting to know you folks."

"Sol, we're proud to be part of the family. Be sure to come out West to see us." No one seemed to notice the loudspeaker's call as their farewells concluded.

Mr. S. M. Groover, telephone, *please*."

"Just a minute, hold everything," Sol announced as he ran over to the nearby courtesy telephone.

Jane knew her husband well. At her first glance into his eyes, she knew something unusual had happened. Sol's face shot out a weak, pale fright.

"Sol, there's been a terrible wreck. We don't know how Terry is, but Nancy's gone," came the neighbor's voice over the phone. Realizing that Sol was probably close to fainting, the voice changed. "Oh, no, Sol, we don't know how Nancy is." But it was already too late.

"There's been an accident. Terry's still here, but we don't know about Nancy," Sol relayed to the others, his right hand shielding the mouthpiece of the receiver.

"No!"

"How bad?"

"What happened?"

Their first reaction was, "It can't be too bad — they'll be all right. Things terribly bad have never happened to us."

It took a minute to decide what to do, and a minute was all they had. My brother-in-law and sisters were told to go on ahead. My parents would remain behind to return home when they found out just how things were.

"I talked to your dad," the officer assured, knowing that trying to explain the chain of calls would be too difficult.

"Be sure and put the call on my bill," I told the officer, incoherently, being relieved that the message had finally reached its destination. "And, please, look after my wife, officer, in Adel."

Just then, another figure approached.

"Terry, I'm Dr. Kirkpatrick," a mild and steady voice announced. "We're going to look you over a bit." Thus far everyone had been supremely kind and good. They made me feel I could trust them.

It was primarily because of this well-known doctor, I later learned, that I was brought to Tifton. He had saved cases in the past that others had given up for lost. Now he had one of the challenges of his lifetime.

First, he began examining my body. One test that normally would have been unbearable, that I didn't feel, being insensitive from shock, was the examination for internal injuries. I looked down at my stomach to see Dr. Kirkpatrick dipping a needle several places into the abdomen.

"Terry, this is the easiest way we have of checking for internal injuries."

"Well, I wouldn't want you to do anything but the easiest."

Then came the methodical diagnosis of surface injuries, head to foot. A nurse at hand, another taking notes, we began. I sort of wandered all this time between consciousness and unconsciousness.

"No teeth missing, bad cut under nose, general face lacerations. We'll need to sew those up," he said. "Terry, we don't want to give you anything for pain so that you can help us identify bad spots." That was all right, feeling paralyzed anyway. I sensed deadly pain in certain areas, though, which identified to me the most critical problems. My chest felt crushed and I could not get a good breath. My arms and legs agonized a deep severe pain, too.

"Multiple fracture of the left arm," he recorded, which was obvious since the bone was projecting through the skin.

"That ring finger on the right hand may have to be amputated. General damage to the right hand. Chest — doesn't seem to be any broken ribs. Your cartilage is broken. Lucky, no ribs are broken, but your sternum is serious," his firm, rhythmic, and steady voice continued. It was like when we used to judge cattle — orderly, not surprised, gently, and matter-of-factly. This attitude, of course, was very healthy for me.

Next, I was rolled into the X-ray room. This took, perhaps, twenty minutes, and unbelievably to them, they could not find a break of either of my legs or my back.

My cousin and best man was due at work the next morning in Chicago, but for some reason Irwin just hadn't gotten started. Being a hospital administrator himself, he put in a call from the Atlanta airport to the doctor to get a report.

"How soon should we be there?" Irwin asked.

"Well, if you want to see him alive, you had better get right down," Dr. Kirkpatrick informed him with frankness.

Dozing on and off, I began to feel quite good. Diagnosis completed, competent hands in control, parents notified, Nancy all right in Adel, I thought, and above all, the tremendous hands of Christ holding everything up. So, when I was asked to sign my admittance slip from my prone position on a stretcher three inches off the floor, I replied, "I can't sign. I can't even move a finger, let alone write my name, but listen, you people are all I have. We live by faith, and I'm trusting that the Lord has control and will allow you to take care of the situation and do whatever you have to do. I don't know what's wrong or what has to be done — you just do whatever you need to."

Three or four attendants were kneeling beside me, and I saw one look to the other, "I think that's a verbal agreement."

"I do, too."

"Listen, if one of you can take a pen," I wanted to joke a little and so softly breathed out, "and hold it between my fingers, and then take the clipboard and hold it up to the pen," they all listened intently wondering what I was going to say, "and then while squeezing the pen very lightly between my fingers, move the clipboard to my name, I'll sign." They got the message and didn't know whether to smile or cry.

With every bit of strength his frame could muster, Sol shakingly put everyone into the family car and pushed the thing toward home. Deadly silence hovered as minds reverted inward with stricken wonderment. Each one had a frightened feeling that he knew what had happened but was afraid to admit it.

Walking into the house, they found people already beginning to gather. Dr. Phillips, the family minister, had rushed over and had taken control of the situation. By now, the four bereaved parents were apprised, at least in general, of the situation. Nancy was dead and I was struggling for life.

Sol placed a call to Tommy, Nancy's oldest brother, to bring himself and the other children right home from a friend's house where they were staying.

"Tommy, I want you to get Mary and Rob and come home." In the middle of an intensely exciting television episode, Tommy came back with, "But, Dad . . ."

"Tommy!" The boy knew by the serious tone of his father's voice that he meant now.

My folks were also sent into near shock, feeling complete helplessness and despair. Irwin had refused to return to Chicago; so within the hour, the three of them departed for Tifton General Hospital, 250 miles south. It seemed the longest 250 mile trek of their lives, not knowing what they would find at the other end.

The three children were shocked by seeing people crying and

moving about the house in confusion as they entered. Dr. Phillips immediately took them to Nancy's room.

"What is he doing here?" they wondered. The last they had seen him was when he performed the wedding the previous evening. They sat down in a row on the bed.

"Children, your sister has gone on to heaven this evening," he so tenderly began. "Terry is hurt real bad and in the hospital."

They were stunned. They could not believe their ears. Nancy? Their oldest sis? The girl they loved and respected almost more than anyone in the whole world?

"Terry, I want you to meet the lady who is going to administer the anesthetic," Dr. Kirkpatrick continued. "She'll be putting you to sleep."

I thought, "How wonderful if we could all pray together before surgery." I looked up and noticed that we were out of the emergency room and in pre-surgery. Then they asked me if they could cut my trousers off to operate.

"Well," I quipped, "they aren't too expensive."

"We need the shirt, too."

"I'd like to keep the shirt," I said bewildered, trying to remember what I had on.

"It's ruined anyway," I heard one tell the other, humoring me.

"Oh, if it's ruined," I seriously replied, "I guess you'd better go ahead," as though it were my decision. Then I heard the "snip, snip, snip," as they cut off the garments.

"Doc," I said, "could we all pray together before we operate?" I am sure, remembering, that usually a patient asks for prayer when in fear, or fear of death.

He came back with, "You are going to be all right."

Not wanting to trouble him, and feeling extremely secure in our Lord's and his hands anyway, I figured I would just pray on my own. What a wonderful bond, I imagined, if all of us, nurses, doctors, and myself, could just join together for a brief one or two sentence prayer. Anyway, out loud as final preparations were laid, I said something like, "Lord, thank You that You have control and that You will see us through this operation. I trust You, Lord, to continue Your control. And thank You, too, Lord, for these thoughtful people You've given to handle things. And Lord — I trust Nancy with You — I don't know about her — I wish I could help her — all we have is You."

I saw them slip the needle into a vein in my foot and inject the Sodium Pentothal. Six seconds and I would be asleep. Darkness was closing in. . . .

I found out later that my lungs were taking a lot of blood, giving me hardly, if at all, a chance to live. The surgery team rapidly set to work, not knowing what would be the result.

Christ had promised to be a faithful Lord and Shepherd. "I will never, no *never* leave thee, nor forsake thee," and "Lo, I am with you *always*, even to the end of the world," He had pledged. This was His chance to prove and verify His word. He had not said it would not be rough, or that we would not die; He just said He would be around when it happened.

16   Flowers and Telegrams

I opened my eyes to see two faces before me. Each had a deadly empty stare — unable to fully comprehend the happening, while earnestly pulling for the one life of the marriage left — the life of their son. It was 2 A.M. My folks had made it down to Tifton under the care of Irwin, and I was reviving from the lengthy and complicated surgery. Once I saw those faces, I felt secure — my folks were with me and would help me. I spent all of my energy in just watching them, and being unable to move, speak, or even keep awake, dropped asleep, not to hear their voices until morning.

"He's been so cooperative," I heard a cheerful voice ring forth on the gloomy, dark Sunday morning. Her remark turned out to be my introduction to the marvelous nurse who cared for me in Tifton. Mrs. Thelma Register worked only special cases, and, enjoying Sundays to herself, could hardly be pried into working on that day, She and Dr. Kirkpatrick had an unwritten, unverbalized agreement, however — it was just one of those things understood and never mentioned. She believed in him as one of the finest surgeons anywhere, and he believed in her as the rarely found, perfect nurse who could not only provide the necessary work for a situation, but for the patient would release a special understanding care and attention — an ingredient which could mean fast or slow recovery, or even in some cases *life* or *death*. I was to need special care twenty-four hours a day, and Dr. Kirkpatrick had ordered before the surgery, "Call Mrs. Register on the phone and ask her to come in."

"Sorry, I won't be able to," was her reply to the hospital.

Five minutes later, another call — "Mrs. Register, this is Dr. Kirkpatrick. Can you be here in one hour?"

After a brief pause and without inquiry, "I'll be there."

So Mrs. Register was at my bedside and cheerfully awakened me early Sunday morning with an optimistic spirit. Her attitude encouraged me to come back to life.

The morning papers extended the gloom cloud bringing horrified reactions even from those who had not known Nancy or me. The *Atlanta Constitution* carried the article on the front page below a special red-printed "GOOD MORNING" to its readers.

Day's Bride Killed

Twenty-five persons — including a bride of one day — have been killed in traffic in Georgia during the long Thanksgiving holiday weekend.

The State Patrol said Nancy Groover Thomas, 21, of Decatur, died in a head-on collision on Interstate 75 near Adel Saturday during a hard rainstorm. Mrs. Thomas was still holding a bouquet of a dozen, long-stemmed red roses when they removed her body. The other car apparently went out of control, crossed the median, and struck the car in which she was riding with her husband, Terry Clifford Thomas, 25. He was hospitalized with critical injuries.

A local city newspaper in rural southern Georgia, the *Albany Sunday Herald,* also brought the horrible news, with an interview from Patrolman Pendleton.

Young Bride, A Dozen Red Roses In Her Lap, Dies In Adel Crash

ADEL — "She had a dozen, long-stemmed red roses in her lap. The ribbon was still tied around them."

That was the way State Highway Patrolman Fred Pendleton of the Highway Patrol described the death of a twenty-one-year-old bride of less than a day, who died instantly in a head-on crash less than a mile north of Adel on Interstate Highway 75 Saturday about 6:30 P.M.

Killed in the acident was Mrs. Nancy Groover Thomas of Decatur. Critically injured was her husband, Terry Clifford Thomas, 25, whose home address is Westchester, Pa.

"I understand they were married only yesterday in Decatur," Pendleton said. "They apparently were on their way to Florida on their honeymoon."

Pendleton said the Thomas car, a German-made compact, was traveling south on I-75, and the McCorvey vehicle, an American-made compact, was going north.

"There was a heavy, localized rainstorm in progress," Pendleton said, "and McCorvey apparently lost control, his car plunging across the median strip and crashing almost head-on into Thomas' car."

The trooper said no charges had been made pending further investigation.

"I've worked many wrecks," Pendleton said, "but seeing this young bride, with the roses in her lap, dead — well, it was kinda rough."

The Associated Press wired the news across the country where many papers carried it.

I lay wilted on my back while Mrs. Register kept busy in the room. I felt like I was crumpled at the bottom of a funnel-shaped hole that had no opening but up. I could not move and was able only to mumble and whisper when trying to talk.

Then Dr. Kirkpatrick came and stood over me. "How is he, Mrs. Register?"

"He is so cooperative," she cheerfully responded. The remark made me feel good.

"I just want to look you over a little, Terry," he told me firmly while bending over to examine some stitches. Then, as if he were merely reporting that the weather was poor, he said, "Terry, I'm sorry to have to tell you this, but your wife was killed in the accident last night." I could not fully comprehend what he was saying — only that it was terrible and something I had already felt. I knew I couldn't reach Nancy and that my folks were nearby, so immediately asked for them.

"I'd like to see my folks," I whispered.

"They'll be along," he said, still examining the stitches. He had given my parents sleeping tablets only hours earlier and wanted them to be able to get as much rest as possible.

A few moments later, I asked again, feeling they would be a big comfort. "I want my folks."

"They will be here in a little while."

I knew I *had* to see them, yet did not understand that they would be so terribly horror-struck — I only thought of myself. "Can you get my folks," I repeated a third time. Dr. Kirkpatrick then realized they were urgently needed. He turned from my bedside immediately and rushed out of the room. I fell asleep and the next thing I knew, I was looking up and watching mother and dad scurrying in.

Mother, seeing the mass of bandages, casts, pulley, and tubes, instinctively tore over to my bedside and almost grabbed me, but was restrained by the fragility of my appearance. She broke into tears and forced her face down next to mine and cried, "Oh, Terry, I'm so sorry, honey, I'm so sorry."

At first, I wondered what for. I could barely move my mouth, so just laid still, feeling sorry for her.

Dad was on the other side of the bed where Mrs. Register had come to the rescue with a box of Kleenex to absorb his tears.

All that day, my mind was pretty fuzzy from the pain-killing narcotics. Shock was still evident, too. A lifetime went by in those first hours. Mrs. Register would awaken me occasionally to breathe deeply from a Bennet Machine which forced a combination of gases into my lungs to help clear them up. The X-rays showed my lungs were filled with blood, and the only way of getting rid of the stuff was by spitting it up. I would breathe through the machine for five minutes and then spit up into a Kleenex in her hand. Neither my folks nor I found out until later that every drop I could emit was priceless, for that meant the difference between life and death.

Often Mother would call out during the day as she sat by my bed, "Some flowers from California; do you want me to read the card?"

"Yes — do," I would weakly utter. After reading, she would

often be called out of the room. Visitors were coming by the scores. The phone rang continually, too, and telegrams came piling in. Nancy's father had grown up in southern Georgia, so hundreds of relatives were nearby. At times, I felt neglected because of the demand on everyone around me.

"We are shocked; our hearts bleed with yours; can we possibly help? Our prayers are for your complete recovery; we thank God that He is more than sufficient for this tragedy; call if we can do anything. Love," wired friends from Washington, D.C.

From the West Coast came these words: "We are praying and grieving with you, hoping Terry will be spared pain. Darling Nancy was very special to be called home so suddenly the last and most beautiful hour of her life. God's blessings."

One by one, Western Union brought the telegrams to the hospital, totalling twenty-five the first day.

Flowers probably meant as much to me at that time as anything. I had grown to marvel at their beauty and appreciated them tremendously as one by one generous and kind family and friends sent their sympathy in this way. Some may say, "Give instead to a worthy cause" — but in those hours I will take the flowers.

Dad and Irwin drove over to the wrecking yard in the afternoon to look at the car. Meanwhile, Sol had driven down with a good friend of the family to take Nancy home. He was dazed as much as anyone, but somehow managed to keep his composure.

He came into my room and walked up to my bedside. I was rather incoherent but vaguely remembered a brief talk.

"You're our boy now, Terry, and as soon as we can get you out of here, you're coming home," he warmly told me. His gentle words provided additional security.

I learned that afternoon that the driver of the other automobile had been admitted to the emergency room the same time I was — but was released that same evening. His injuries were minor.

All the while I was very conscious of the presence of Jesus Christ. I sensed Him closely alongside, with surety that He would not be leaving for any reason. Instinctively, I felt He would be using my life and mouth, and the lives and mouths of others, to release His *good news* with power and abandonment as never before. I was conscious that somehow He would turn this tragic mess into immeasurable good — that some way, somehow, the world would be further enlightened as to His power and strength — and of the fact that He had come to this planet and would come again because He loved it — because He loved the people — because He loved each person!

When things quieted down a little, I asked, "Mother, can you read for me from the Bible?"

"Yes, Terry, let me get it."

A Bible was provided handily in the drawer near the bed, and then she asked, "Where do you want me to read?"

"Oh, I don't care — anywhere — how about Psalm 23 — and then John 14." I could not listen for a long span, only pick up a word or two at a time — having been drugged so by painkillers — but the sound of the poetry and the words of Jesus flowing by were soothing. Mother was trying so hard to read well. I honestly think she was afraid it was my last day.

Before leaving that evening, the three of us — mother, dad, and I spent some time praying together.

Monday came and was quieter than Sunday. Needles were still poked in me by the case until I was sure I had become a pin cushion. I developed bed sores on the bottoms of my heels and elbows. My joints were still black and blue, and I could hardly move, being confined to my back. It was on Monday that I became conscious of certain injuries which until then had gone unnoticed.

I realized that my chest was hooked in traction by a chain, and was told the pulley I could see, looking up from my back, was weighted with six pounds of water. My left arm was hooked to another pulley with a cast up to the shoulder, and my right arm was in a cast and bandaged completely over the hand. I noticed a tube stuck into a vein in my foot feeding me intravenously, and along with a catheter, I had a tube continually pumping my stomach. Long-distance phone calls came in, however, as steadily as they had Sunday. I only had strength to take one that day, and it was from Randy in D.C.

"There's a call from Randy Stime," Mrs. Register told me.

"Well, let me talk to him!" I said.

"Do you think you can?"

"Sure — if you hold the phone to my ear." Mrs. Register had a sneaky way of helping patients progress.

"Hey, old man, what's ya' up to?" I said.

"What? How are you?"

"Not bad — just a few bumps — be out of here in a couple of days!" I noticed Mrs. Register frown with an impish smirk.

"Do you want me to come down?"

"No, Randy, but I sure want to see you soon."

"Well, I want you to spend some time relaxing here with me when you are up to it." That made me feel good. We soon ended our conversation and Monday was history.

Tuesday morning came and again the portable X-ray machine and technicians were called in. A while later, Dr. Kirkpatrick entered with a broad smile.

"Terry, you're going to make it." He could hardly believe that first, that my lungs were cleared, and secondly, so soon.

Irwin was still there and came in after reading the reports.

"Terry, we've got you out of the woods."

"What do you mean, 'out of the woods?'" I said from my back.

"You're going to make it!"

"I could have told you that three days ago!"

"Irwin," I said in confidence, "I think you'd better get back to your job."

"What do you think about your folks?" He had been helping them tremendously.

"I think they are all right now."

"Are you sure?"

"Yes — you go now — and 'cuz — thanks a lot."

There was not a hand to shake, but he gave my left foot a squeeze from the end of the bed, took a last, long look, turned, and walked out. I could tell he didn't want me to see him shed tears.

I was still confined to my back, but was beginning to move my head slightly from side to side. All I had seen was the ceiling, and I had no idea what was beyond the door or outside the hospital — though my curiosity was rising fast.

That afternoon we began to think about the funeral 200 miles away on Wednesday, the next day. It was a blessing in disguise for me to be confined to bed, for in my frame of mind, it would have broken my heart to see Nancy dead.

My mind and heart felt tender and scared. The severe shock condition had left an aftereffect. Dr. Kirkpatrick and his team knew this and had news articles and mail censored, that I might not be jolted again to a stupor.

My folks did not know if they should leave me alone on Wednesday and drive to Decatur. I told them I would make the decision and tell them early the next morning.

17 The Funeral

As I woke up Wednesday morning, somehow my mind focused on Nancy's comment several months earlier. "What a kind and loving Father we have and how I long to see Him face to face."

"Nancy's really with You now, Lord, isn't she," I softly replied. But my emotions still had not fully responded to the loss. I was not totally aware of the fact that I would never see Nancy again.

It was still dark a few minutes later when my folks walked into the room. They knew I needed them nearby, but the funeral was in Decatur that day, too.

"Are you ready to go?" I asked.

"Do you want us to?" mother asked.

"Yes, I want you to be there."

"Are you sure?"

"Yes, you go, I'll be all right — and the minister from town here — Pastor Bradford — you said he'd be in often."

"Well, okay."

"I'll miss you two — hope you don't get back too late."

They arrived in Decatur in plenty of time. The first thing they did was walk up to the casket in the front of the church and solemnly stand beside the lifeless remains of their daughter-in-law. Somehow, she didn't seem to be Nancy. That lively girl who was so excited to help catch a salmon, or to pull in the crab from Puget Sound; that girl who was so in love with their son was gone.

131

Yes — indeed, the true person had only been encased in that body — and that inner person was indestructible — she was still alive — but, oh, so hard to realize that now!

Eventually people began filing into the sanctuary. Among those earliest came some of Nancy's dearest friends. One had said Nancy was the closest friend she had ever had.

Another had said she was the most faithful to the Lord she had known.

A college roommate wrote:

"I have read that beauty lies in the eyes of the beholder — which I feel is true — and that behind beauty lies happiness. I want to share two of the times I saw Nancy look truly beautiful. Once was when she gave her testimony at a youth crusade, and the other was the night she was married. The first was when she was testifying of her trust and faith in Christ, and the second was when she was marrying the man whom she felt 'incomplete' without.

"So Nancy lived a truly rich, full, and beautiful life. Not many women of twenty can say this, nor many of sixty.

"She knew what she wanted from life, and what she wanted to give, and she succeeded."

The organist — the same one who played for the wedding — sat at the console and began pressing the keys to bring out the deep tones from the pipes. The entire senior class from Wesleyan arrived and solemnly filled several rows.

There were so many flowers that the front of the church was camouflaged with freshly cut buds, blossoms, and wreaths.

Nancy's family entered — father and mother, Tommy and Rob, and little sis, Mary.

The organ tones swelled a little stronger now, and then suddenly they stopped. Then silence — except for an occasional rustle or sniffle. The auditorium was packed beyond capacity. Then, suddenly, yet from only medium volume, came the familiar melody which had been played at the wedding just a half week previous, "How Great Thou Art." "Oh, Lord, my God," you could hear the words sing in your heart. "When I in awesome wonder," — volume and intensity rose.

Then at the chorus it became louder and more victorious.

Tears were filling eyes. "Then sings my soul, my Savior God to Thee — how — great — THOU — art —" and with power and fervor — as though Nancy was truly still alive — the last line rang forth thunderously — "how — great — Thou — art, — HOW — GREAT — THOU — ART!!"

The music stopped; the scent of flowers filled the air.

Dr. Phillips and Carl Wilson, the two ministers who had performed the wedding, entered from the same door Irwin and I had squirmed through just four evenings before.

My parents sat quietly — hardly believing what was going on before them.

Dr. Phillips walked to the podium and broke the silence with a prayer.

"We Thy children lean upon Thee, we seek Thee, God of all comfort and the Father of mercy. . . ." Next they sang a hymn, and then Carl Wilson stood.

"One of the staff members who worked a great deal with Nancy last year made the comment that of all the girls she had worked with, she felt that Nancy had the most consistent Christian life of any that she had known. This passage was her favorite, and, I believe, is the secret for that life. I read this at the request of Terry, because it was her favorite passage. And this was her favorite translation of it:

"'I am the real vine, and my Father is the gardener. He breaks off every branch in me that does not bear fruit, and prunes every branch that does bear fruit, so that it will bear more fruit. You have been made clean already by the message I have spoken to you. Remain in union with me, and I will remain in union with you. Unless you remain in me you cannot bear fruit, just as a branch cannot bear fruit unless it remains in the vine.

"'I am the vine, you are the branches. Whoever remains in me, and I in him, will bear much fruit; for you can do nothing without me. Whoever does not remain in me is thrown out, like a branch, and dries up; such branches are gathered up and thrown into the fire, where they are burned. If you remain in me, and my words remain in you, then you will ask for anything you wish, and you shall have it. This is how my Father's glory is shown'" (*Good News for Modern Man*).

After reading, Carl Wilson looked up at the congregation, eyes red, yet with a visible spirit of hope.

"I feel this particular passage, which speaks of fruit bearing, certainly speaks of Nancy's life, and I would like to take this occasion to say one or two things. I came to know Nancy extremely well last year as she worked in some of our youth crusade efforts up in Fayetteville, and then for a considerable time over a period of months in Macon. Her desire was to help other young people know Jesus Christ as she knew Him, to have the joy of the abundant life which Christ gives both now and throughout eternity.

"And I feel confident, somehow, as I stand with you today, that as in her life so in her death, she would have me emphasize to each of you the importance of knowing Jesus Christ personally as your Savior and as your Lord. I trust that you will search your own hearts, and if you have not come to know Christ, I urge you to invite Him into your life.

"There will be times when we will be tested. It is easy enough to trust God when we can walk in the light and we can see where He is leading us. It is when we walk in the darkness that we have the true test of whether we trust Him or just ourselves. And I would remind you that while many of us cannot understand this, God's wisdom is above our own, and even Jesus at one time cried out on the cross, 'Why?' Yet, He could also say, 'Father, into Thy hands I commit My Spirit.' It is, indeed, a wonderful thing to be able to trust God. He is our Creator, He has planned our lives, and His plan is best."

Rev. Wilson concluded and Dr. Phillips stood and solemnly faced the congregation.

"It was once said that no one really begins to live until he learns how to put death in its proper place. God has put death in its place in the person of His Son, Jesus Christ. We believe in God the Father Almighty and we believe also in Jesus Christ who was crucified, dead and buried, and was raised from the dead. And who, really, in a sense, has abolished death and brought life and immortality to life in the Gospel. And this we must do today; we must look death straight in the face and put it in its proper place. It is a fact. You cannot miss it. We may often read the statistics of death in the papers without it becoming personal. But when it becomes intimately personal, we cannot ignore it; we cannot disguise it; it comes. It comes when we least expect it. No one knows what the next day will bring, but death for a Christian is a door, not a wall; it's an open door into the presence of God; it is a beginning, not an ending. It is not the end of existence; it is the fulfillment of the purpose of existence. It is a complete fulfillment, not a frustration, of God's purpose.

"In the eleventh chapter of Hebrews, 'Abel offered an acceptable sacrifice unto God, and by it, he being dead,' said the writer, 'still speaks.'

"This is a thought which kept coming back to my mind as I thought of Nancy. She still speaks; she speaks of many things to us; many good things, but, especially, of Jesus Christ, who is the same yesterday, today, and forever. Is He not the same today as He was on Friday evening? Is He not the same tomorrow as He was on Saturday? Is He not one who only lived to make an intercession for us? Is He not one who said, "Blessed be they who mourn, for they shall be comforted?' Did He not look death in the face on the cross and put it in its proper place, even when He said, 'My God, My God, why hast Thou forsaken Me?' He was a man of sorrows and acquainted with grief. And did He not die that we might live? Did He not love all men everywhere? Was He willing that any should perish? And so we look to the name of Christ and God our Father; and this is His servant, who, being dead, still speaks to us of Him. . . . Therefore, today, we give thanks to God for this faith, for this, His servant, and say blessed are the dead who die in the Lord."

After prayer, the congregation sang another hymn and the organ continued through the benediction. Then folks slowly began standing — some starting up the aisle to the rear. No one really wanted to leave.

Most of them went to the cemetery in procession. Sadness seemed to be fading. A beam of victory was brightening the atmosphere.

Nancy's casket was slowly lowered into the concrete vault. It was still raining — leaves were blowing and the grass was brown — it was a barren, desolate November afternoon.

Suddenly the tomb was shut — sealed — covering the body of the precious Nancy — — but that was not Nancy down there.

Yes, her real person was still alive!

Back in the hospital, I was having a terrible day — my worst so far. My life was reviving, and little pains — at least minor until that point — were increasing. It seemed the folks would never return, but Mrs. Register was so good. Sometimes I had a hard time telling if she was my nurse or my buddy — she could be a tease at the right moment.

It got dark again; Mrs. Register's shift was over and she was gone. And my folks still weren't back.

18 "Oh, Get Him on His Feet"

They started me on a light liquid diet Wednesday night. I had just finished eating jello when mother and dad walked in. They seemed almost more anxious to see me than I was to see them.

"Terry, it was just beautiful — and the Lord — He was definitely honored," were mother's first words.

"I know it was good," I answered.

They were completely worn out, so they left after a half hour, but not before we prayed together and entrusted the night to Him.

Joe, my night nurse, and I were together later that evening when another gasping pain struck. I coughed — I gasped — I coughed again — then, "Oh — oh — oh — my chest!"

Joe ran for the doctor and he was quickly at my bedside.

I had jolted the plate loose that was anchored to my chest and suspended by pulleys and traction, and my chest felt as though it were caving in. Quickly the portable X-ray unit was wheeled in to take some shots.

In a few minutes, Dr. Kirkpatrick returned.

"Terry, I'm going to take this thing off — I was going to in the morning anyway. I know it hurts, and it will for a day or so — you've been used to the weight against it — and, of course, you know your chest took a terrible blow."

The steering post of the car had been driven, on impact, like a nail, deep into my chest, while at the same moment my body lurched forward.

137

I began to get used to the pain, and being restless from just laying could hardly sleep. So Joe and I talked — as we had begun to do nights earlier. Joe had read some philosophy on his own, and much of the Bible, too, so we had several ideas to discuss. But this night our conversation led us more to the man — Jesus Christ.

"I know there is something different about Jesus, but why do you call Him Lord?" Joe asked.

My tongue had been deeply slashed about midway back, and it seemed to grow more painful as days wore on. But something deep inside urged me to talk.

"Well, basically, because He did something no one else has ever done."

"What do you mean?"

"I mean being a sacrifice. We try like crazy to overcome our sin by our own efforts — sometimes through being good, sometimes through being religious — but He died to fill in the part that's missing."

"How do you mean?"

"I mean like a bridge across a river! You try to build it yourself and you can't — and He comes to be the link you couldn't complete!"

"Okay, I understand — but how does man fit in?"

"We all need to open up our lives to God and receive this gift — this sacrifice — this link. He's already done the work — it's just a matter of acknowledging it before it's put in my account."

"Ya?"

"Ya! Like the bank — you can have the million bucks, but it's not in your account 'til you let God put it there."

It was one in the morning when Joe and I finished talking, and before we were through, he truly opened his life up to Christ. It was neat knowing he was forgiven now, too, for everything past, present, and future — that he was a brother. I guess his skin was black, too, but who noticed?

Morning came and the folks arrived as usual. Still, I was

restricted to bed. I felt sure I could walk if they would give me a chance, but the hospital expected me to be in bed for at least another week.

Letters continued pouring in, and by Thursday, my mail stack was higher than all the rest of the hospital's put together. One family began a typical letter:

This is such a hard letter to write. We want you to know that we're with you in thoughts and prayers. If there's anything we can do, please let us know.

A packet of twelve cards came from a local congregation expressing their sympathy and encouragement. A boy in prison, who had opened up his life to Christ while there, wrote a heartwarming letter. Mother would read a batch in the morning, another in the afternoon, and again in the evening. A kind, personal letter came from our congressman.

One that was very special came from a dear friend.

Our dear brother,

We want you to know our hearts are with you in thanking the Lord for Nancy and the privilege she now has of being in the presence of the One she loves and serves.

Death is a tragedy only to the world — to us it is a victory, the ultimate hope of each one of us.

I know the question "Why?" must be in your mind, Terry. All possible answers and in an insoluble dilemma, except the sure fact, He knows! "That He who died for us, whether we are awake or asleep, we may LIVE TOGETHER WITH HIM!" Oh, the triumph in those words.

As your needs have permeated our minds for twenty-four hours now, the Lord reminded me that she will spend her first Christmas in His bodily presence.

Then another friend wrote:

"I know Nancy is one of the most beautiful angels somewhere out there — in her wedding gown for Christ."

Sadness and cheer! Everyone felt terrible, but many tried to help brighten things.

Friday came, and as yet, I had not even sat up in bed. I did not know how much longer I could put up with confinement and was crabby and curt when awakened. The folks had been keeping a steady, rapid pace, so had said they would sleep late.

I had been having a little trouble, and the hospital did not know what course of action to take. Mrs. Register said, with a twinkle in her eyes, "Terry, I'm going to see what I can do with Dr. Kirkpatrick." She knew my improvement was rapid, but the doctor had previously said I would not be out of bed for at least twelve days — six had passed.

Mrs. Register left the room for a few minutes in search of the doctor. He was just ready to step into surgery when she found him.

"What do you think we should do with Terry?" she asked.

"Well, keep working at it." Dr. Kirkpatrick started toward the door. Mrs. Register did not say a word. Dr. Kirkpatrick opened the door, put one foot in, and then turned; he noticed Mrs. Register had not moved.

He paused — seemed blank for a moment — then gruffly said, "Oh, get him on his feet."

Mrs. Register came bounding into my room and started moving things around.

"You're getting up — it won't be what you expect, but you'll be on your feet!"

"Oh — man — really? Help me up — let's go!" I said from my back.

Mrs. Register called in a male nurse, and they slowly elevated me to a seated position. Then they carefully dropped my legs over the side of the bed — I was sitting up. I paused for a moment and looked around. I stared out the window — it was different out — new.

"Okay, now, Terry — we'll help you." With one on either side, I slowly and gradually began straightening my joints and shifting my weight to my feet. I heard my ankles and knees break forth with crackles and pops.

"Easy — easy."

"I can do it!" I told them.

I was standing — still in a rather crouched position — but I was up!

Then, with their help, I shuffled forward a couple steps. It felt good — but so tiring.

"I guess I better sit down for a minute," I weakly said.

"Certainly — you've done a lot already!"

I felt proud — didn't realize I was asking for bigger trouble by recovering. About an hour and a half later, we decided to try it again.

I got up. This time Mrs. Register had a large walker by the bed, it looked like a cage.

"This is what makes it all worthwhile," she said.

I stood up again and braced myself on the walker. I started shuffling a few steps and found I could move. I began a beeline for one spot — the door — I had to see what was outside. Mrs. Register was holding onto me, right at my side.

We walked into the hall without saying a word. I looked up and down the hall trying to figure which way was which, and then started up.

Then the realization hit me — I was on my way. I suddenly felt like I was leading the Fifth Avenue Easter Parade. I could feel some tears from the inside getting ready to burst. I must have looked a mess. My face had gone unshaven for a week and my hair was so ratted it was impossible to comb.

I barely heard Mrs. Register say, "Terry, I didn't realize you were so tall." I kept shuffling forward, I felt like a king.

Then I heard my folks' voices from around the corner.

"How is he this morning, doctor?"

"Take a look for yourself."

I kept shuffling forward — tears proudly streaming down my cheeks.

My parents stepped into sight. Their faces were blank — empty — staring — then, all at once, proud smiles beamed as they realized. They had not expected me to be out of bed for at least another week.

"Well, look at that," mother said.

I kept inching forward.

"Good morning," I said as I shuffled by, not even looking their way. I knew they would be crying, too.

I took two more walks that day and began to enjoy looking out the window. I had been imprisoned and could now anticipate release.

I do not know when I have ever sensed the presence of Christ more powerfully than that week. It was as though He was the most real person there. I did not feel I needed to pray or meditate to sense Him — He was overwhelming. Perhaps it was a foretaste of eternity.

Surgery was to be done on my left arm Saturday morning, and just after the "happy shot" had been administered, the entire Groover family arrived from Atlanta. It had taken dad over an hour to shave my face, making his way around various scabs and scars, but at least I was presentable when the in-laws entered. I was whisked off to surgery, however, only minutes after their arrival.

Setback again! Couldn't get up — couldn't walk — that was the story for another post-operative twenty-four hours. It seemed I had spent my life in Tifton General, but it had been just a week.

On Sunday afternoon, Dr. Kirkpatrick took mother and dad aside.

"Had you considered taking Terry home?"

"It hadn't occurred to us!"

"There is a possibility. Terry has improved far beyond expectations. I guess you know, we didn't even expect him to live."

The folks didn't know how to reply.

"By the way, what is this 'yogurt' he likes?"

"Two years ago he began a whole new way of eating — natural foods — it's really made him a whole lot healthier, and yogurt is part of it."

"Well, let me explain this now. I can possibly release Terry tomorrow. What I'd like to do is make arrangements at the Decatur Hospital, and he can be thoroughly examined upon arrival. If he checks out okay, he can go on to Bellingham. How does that sound?"

"If you think he's able, we'd like to do it that way — very much!"

A little while later, mother broke the news. "Terry, had you thought of going to Bellingham?"

I didn't know what to say. "You mean now?"

"Dr. Kirkpatrick thinks there's a possibility."

"Well, I'm well enough — I mean, I'm able — there's no question about that."

Nine o'clock Monday morning, the red and white Cadillac ambulance rolled up to the emergency entrance of Tifton General. Two uniformed officials got out and marched briskly towards my room.

Upstairs, dozens of papers were being signed, bags being packed, and what seemed a million good-byes being said. One special word came from the lady who had admitted me into the hospital.

"Terry, I just had to come and say good-bye — and tell you that I knew you were a Christian when they first rolled you in the door, by the sweet smile you had on your face." It further confirmed the tremendous presence of Christ. I had been in no shape to relax or smile; I guess it had just happened, and I didn't even know about it. I was told that literally thousands of lives in the area had been affected by the evidence of God's power.

"Fresh air — wow, it's chilly," I said as we broke through the door to the ambulance. Nothing but warm, heated air had entered my lungs for ten days.

I tried to see all I could in pulling out of Tifton. I felt as though it was nearly my home, but I had not even had a glimpse of it until now. We rolled out onto the Interstate and cruised toward our Decatur rendezvous.

It seemed like real progress — from bed confinement to standing — and standing to shuffling — and now shuffling to riding. I thought for a moment of the crash, but we didn't pass the spot. It was further south.

The ride was quite tiring, but eventually we pulled into the doctor's office in Decatur, where Sol and Jane were waiting. After an examination, the doctor stood back and thoroughly scrutinized me.

"I can make it," I told him. He did not seem to be so sure.

So Sol, Dad, and I sat down with the doctor for a little conference.

"As far as I'm concerned, it depends on his attitude," the doctor said.

"We'd love to keep him here," Sol broke in.

"Well, it would probably be best if he could be at home, but the trip could be *very* long — possibly too much," the doctor added.

"I know I'm able," I said.

"Okay, Terry, I want you to rest well tonight and see how you feel in the morning. If there's any question, come and see me then; otherwise you can go."

"Fine," I said, and I knew I would feel fine in the morning.

The ambulance took us back to the motel we had stayed in two weeks before, and I quickly got into bed. Both families were nearby all evening, before saying final good-byes once again.

I guess I had been so busy improving that I had not had time to let the pain and sadness of losing Nancy strike my emotions full force.

I was still on pain pills, but pains were popping up all over — especially in my knees and hips. It was inconvenient, too, to lug the heavy casts around on my arms — especially uncomfortable while sleeping.

Morning came and a cab pulled up to chauffeur us to the airport.

We were met at the main door by a United Airlines hostess with a wheelchair. I hated to use it, but knew the day ahead was long and dared not attempt overextending. United had reserved extra seats for us and taken out the divider between to give ample room for maximum comfort. The take-off was gentle, and within minutes we were looking back at Decatur. A strange sensation flooded me.

"I came here to get Nancy, and I've left her behind — forever. This must be a bad dream."

But between taking pills and changing planes in St. Louis, I was kept too occupied to think further or let the emotional response control me.

Seattle found another waiting crew, including a small reception of friends and my sister — all of them in tears. The drive from the airport to home added the straw of exhaustion that nearly broke the camel's back, but we made it.

It was upon arriving home that floods of grief began battering with their powerful and forceful turbulence. The last time I had been home, Nancy and I were together. I made my way upstairs to the room I would be staying in — Nancy had slept there last summer.

Realization rushed in again — suddenly I could see Nancy laying there on the bed. I remembered coming in in the mornings and waking her — or saying good-night. I could not hold back the tears — they were forcing themselves to the corners of my eyes. I could see Nancy turning over — so cute — so beautiful — so perfect. I could hear her sheepishly saying, "Good morning, sweetheart."

I started to cry — I couldn't hold it back. Then I sobbed — it felt terrible inside — sick — something was missing, and I realized rationally, for the first time, I would never see Nancy again.

After finally getting to bed, I again sensed the Lord Jesus' overwhelming presence. Thousands were praying — I felt it.

Then morning came — it was the worst morning of my life. Being accustomed to early hospital hours coupled with the three-hour time change, I awakened at four in the morning. It was black out, and of course no one was up in the house. I lay in bed with my arms propped up — they hurt. My legs were aching, too. There was only one solution and that was to get up.

I did, but found I was lost. I was alone — no one was there. The folks were so exhausted I dare not waken them. Finally, I found a quiet Tennessee Ernie Ford album and turned the stereo on low. That helped.

Then I shufflingly paced — tried to read — nothing helped.

I took Nancy's picture and looked straight into her eyes. I felt myself beginning to weep again and to reach out for her, but she was gone — I knew that now. I was finally realizing that I would never ever hold her again or talk with her. I don't know how long I wept, but it felt better to have it behind.

About six, I wandered into the kitchen, found paper and pen, and slowly and meticulously, still being in two casts, began a letter to Sol and Jane.

19 Walking — No, Flying Again

Dear family,

We made it home just fine last night. It is now six A.M. — nine A.M. in Atlanta — and no one is up here — the house is very dreary.

The realization of missing our beloved girl is at its worst — it's suddenly rushed upon me with terrible fervor. I don't know if I can stand it. But I guess I will have the strength — His strength — yes, I sense it, but sometimes I feel I'd rather sulk than take it. It's so good He understands anyway and won't withhold Himself just because I am in a mood.

I'm very anxious to get back into the New Testament. I know that this has removed layers of chaff from my spiritual eyes, and there will be much more to see now than ever before.

I guess one thing I'm already seeing is the great emphasis it places on the "Kingdom of God" or the life to come — I mean that I'm starting to see that the big thing to Jesus and to Paul was the fantastic life ahead for us. If we realized this, we would be relieved of the petty worries that try to frustrate us in this life. It'll help us, too, to look clearly at our goal ahead, not at the trivialities here.

I just wanted to write you — you know how much you all mean to me, and I'll look forward to seeing you soon.

Love,
Terry

We went to the doctor that morning, and as suspected, I was going to have to have another operation on my left arm immediately. Arrangements were made, and I was admitted to the hospital that afternoon — Room 810.

Letters and cards continued pouring in and were a great consolation. An older friend dearly wrote:

> Words cannot express, or human emotions emanate, the deep and genuine sympathy I feel for you, Terry. Life's shroud is unyielding and honors no amends; but there is a light in the offing and that is Christ our Lord.

Many letters and cards came from strangers, too, in response to the newspaper articles around the country.

"I don't know what comfort a stranger can be to you — but I felt I must write a note of sympathy and encouragement."

Others wrote how they wished that they themselves could carry the burden.

A friend said:

"Though one wants to do something at a time like this, there doesn't seem to be anything tangible to do — but the intangible prayer."

Others could see the victorious implications.

"Your faith — triumph to God — makes a liar out of Satan."

Arrangements were in order now, including the preparations for surgery the next day. By my hospital bed, amongst the flowers people were sending, I placed Nancy's portrait, which caught the eye of another girl that evening.

Pattie was a young student nurse and had read the account of the auto crash in the paper. Late that night she was sent into my room for final check, and we chatted for a few minutes as she performed her duties. Then she noticed the portrait.

"Is that your wife?" she gently asked.

"Yes."

"She must have been wonderful!"

"Why do you say that?" I queried.

"I can just tell."

"Well, you are so very right. She was fabulous — and we had so much together."

"You seem to be taking it quite well." She could perceive a ray of victory in the tragic storm.

"Listen, Pattie, I know you have lots to do, but when you are free, come back; I want to tell you about it."

"Okay — I mean, I'll be back then in a little bit — I am quite interested."

An hour and a half passed, and it got to be eleven-thirty, but Pattie returned.

"I thought you might be asleep by now," she said·quietly.

"I've been waiting for you."

"Oh, good."

"Pattie, I said I wanted to tell you about it."

"Yes."

"What I wanted to tell you was why I'm able to take the shock. I don't mean it isn't hard, but why I am able to face it."

"It is unusual."

"You see, Nancy and I simply had put our trust in God — I mean, first of all, for Him to forgive us of our sins and to give us eternal life."

I could see by her face she did not comprehend what I was saying.

"You see, this gives us two practical buffers in the situation I'm in now."

"Yes?"

"One — I know Nancy is with Christ now because He promised that we would never die if we believe in Him; and two — He is present with me now with great comfort, that is in His Spirit and in His people. You know, through the love and kindness of others who believe in Him — it helps more than I can say."

"Terry, that's so wonderful. I've tried Christ, but He just hasn't worked for me at all." I sensed a sincere frustration in her statement.

"What did you try?"

"I've tried following the rules — tried going to church — oh, I've tried it all."

"What about forgiveness?"

"Oh, I've committed myself too many times."

"And dedicated?"

"And dedicated!"

"Listen, Pattie, I know what you mean — Nancy and I had, too — and it failed us."

"Then what gave you what you had?"

"Christ."

"What do you mean?"

"Jesus Christ — the person! You see, so many of our efforts are just that — *attempts* to please Christ — *efforts* from inside *ourselves* to help Christ — be they moral efforts or religious works."

"What about commitment?"

"Commitment is saying, 'I will promise You, Christ, to do such and so' — be it live a better life, go to church, and so on."

"Yes?"

"And naturally, we eventually fail. Some don't think they do, though, and become proud, and they love to scorn the ones who have failed — makes 'em feel good — elevates 'em."

"Terry, this is beginning to make sense. But how do you truly find Christ?"

"He usually comes when someone tells you about Him. And they'll tell you that He is simply standing at the entrance to your life, alertly for you to invite Him in. All you have to do is let Him — and then you'll know He's inside because He promised He would be — and you'll just have a certain assurance, too."

"I've honestly never heard it that way before."

"Pattie, it's really that simple — tonight, now, don't hesitate, let Him in — just hand Him yourself — not what you can *do* or what you *have* — just *you*. Christ's enemy will come and tell you this is a hoax and try to deceive you — so, it's best you do it soon."

I could see by her face that her deep, inner person was experiencing a great struggle, but also I could see her face begin to shine and glow — I knew that the Lord's voice had been heard.

I soon fell asleep from the sleeping pill.

It was 7 A.M. when they woke me up. Breakfast? No, another sleeping pill. UGH! I stayed awake long enough to see them wheel me into surgery.

I saw the doctor's masked face over me, and when I heard him say, "Let's get started," I said, "Hey, I'm still awake."

No one laughed, but then they poked their needle into a vein to flood my brain with Sodium Pentothal.

I slept nearly all day and all night. I woke up a few times, once to see Pattie standing over me.

"Oh, Pattie," I mumbled, "what time is it?"

"Ten-thirty."

"You mean at night?" I weakly replied.

"Yes," she chuckled.

"Say, how are things?"

I could see a great wide smile.

"They're fantastic!" I knew she had opened her life up to Christ.

"I went home last night and called my folks. I hadn't seen them for over a month — I've hated them. But, Terry, I felt such love for them. They came right over to my apartment, and we cried together with joy. Oh, I just can't say how. . . ."

I succumbed again to the pull of sleep, but I was rejoicing in my heart over the joy in Pattie and her family. Though every day would not be like eating whipped cream, I knew that Pattie had Christ, too, and that He would never leave her and would guide her along to trust Him just as much through dark days as bright. I knew He was just as dependable for her life as He had been for mine.

Word began to spread that something unusual was happening in 810. Eventually, I began to walk a little again, and eat, too. Then, another evening, another nurse with whom I had become acquainted in the few days I had been there dropped into 810.

"Hi, Lynn," I greeted.

"Good evening, Terry," she said as she pulled the blinds shut.

"How are things your way?"

"Oh, fine." I wasn't convinced, I felt she did not want me to be.

"Well, I'm coming along — sure great to have good help," I casually remarked.

"A lot of folks complain about the help."

"You didn't get what I meant."

"What do you mean?"

"God." I dropped the bomb.

Lynn did not even flinch. She continued her routine, by this time counting my pulse as she held my wrist. Then she looked into my eyes — I could see hers were strained.

"You have some of us pretty shook up."

"Oh?"

"Yes, Pattie and I have been talking. She says her whole life is changed."

"Oh?" I grinned. By now she was pumping up the arm band to check my blood pressure.

"She says her whole family is."

"Oh?" I said again, casually.

"She says you talked to her about Christ."

"Oh, ya, I guess I did." Maybe I was being too casual. Lynn was through and started for the door.

"Lynn!" I said. She stopped and turned my way.

"Come here a minute." She did. "Do you have a minute?"

"Yes."

"Are you having some problems?" I softly asked.

"Well — yes," she shyly replied.

"I have lots of time."

"Oh, it's nothing specific. I'm just not happy."

"Did Pattie tell you what I told her about Christ?"

"Yes."

"Did you give Christ a try?"

She seemed confused — worried. "I have tried Christ — and He's worked." We talked slowly and quietly — no hurry. "The trouble is lately I've let Him down."

"Oh?"

"Yes, I've run out on Him."

"And now you're unhappy."

"Yes, and I don't know what to do."

"I don't have any formulas to give you — seems like God never gave us a bunch of quick little things we can say or do to straighten us out. But let me ramble on a minute, and maybe the Lord will speak to us."

I could see serious searching in her eyes.

"There're always two voices that will talk to us once we are Christians."

"Yes?"

"One is our Lord — Jesus Christ, and the other is our enemy — Satan."

"Hum."

"Yes, and he will speak deceptively of our Lord. He will tell us Christ is inadequate. He will tell us Christ is inadaquate to take care of our sins — that we still have some. Yes, that we are still guilty! He will use anything he can to get our eyes off Christ and onto ourselves — and our shortcomings. He'll tell us we are defeated.

"Christ, on the other hand, comes with a powerful voice of assurance — telling us we are forgiven — that our sin is wiped out — nailed to the cross — and that now He is our lawyer defending our case, and that we are victorious.

"The problem comes when we begin listening to our enemy. Before long, we feel guilty — separated from God. We feel it's worthless to pray or to read the Bible. But we try, and the harder we try, the farther we fall, and we get miserable and just don't know what to do."

"Terry," Lynn broke in, "that's me — exactly."

"Okay, we need to simply listen to the words of our Lord, and to believe Him."

"I think I sort of understand."

"Notice, Lynn, I'm not giving you a package deal. God is personal with you — He loves you very much — you are His daughter, my sister, and He has words fitly chosen for you."

I could see her eyes begin to brighten a little.

"Lynn, I think the best thing for us would be to go together to Him and talk it over."

"Oh, wonderful." I could see her shyness fading. We did pray. We turned the problem over to Christ and we thanked Him — we thanked Him for forgiveness, for the cross, for the gift of coming into our lives, and for winning the battles of life for us.

There was no question that we felt a bond of unity as we prayed, and I noticed that her life definitely began to be different. It was a few weeks later when I received a little note in the mail:

"Thanks, Terry, so much for letting God use you — I'm really enjoying life with Him now."

I knew she *really* was thanking *God* and that she knew I was a brother — a servant of Christ — and that she just wanted us to be able to thank Him together.

Recovery began to come, and I knew one day, perhaps after several months, I would be nearly normal again.

It seemed already that the life Nancy had given had left a door to eternity open behind her, and that many, because of the testimony of her life, were entering in. Was it worth it? I did not know, but I guess I had to say yes, in view of eternity. But for now, I wanted her — I needed her. Yet, the pillow of Christ was always there to cry on — the firmness of His strong arm was always around my shoulder when I needed Him.

I heard from Atlanta. They too were missing her terribly, but finding the great God of all comfort as never before. Somehow, He was bringing us through. I reminded myself that once I was able enough to return to Atlanta, I would chip in Nancy's stone the words of Paul: "For to me to live *is* Christ, and to die *is* gain." I knew this would remind me, Nancy's family, and all who passed by the Decatur cemetery that even at her peak in life — at the brink of her happiest hours — death opened the door to a still better life.

20 Dear Nancy

One evening as I was recovering, I let my mind wander and dream. "What if Nancy and I could be together — just for a little while — what would we say?"

My first reaction was, "I'd love her — what a thrill!" But then, "It would be for such a short while, and she would quickly go back to where she is now. And I would have to stay here — so — what would be most worthwhile saying?"

My mind began to construct the scene — perhaps in the evening — maybe sunset — I'd be alone.

"Nancy, I'm so glad to see you, and I know we've so much to say — I mean about life — and death — and all that's happened."

I knew we would be excited to see each other; we would not have to tell each other of our devotion and how much we had missed each other.

"Nancy, the hardest thing I've been facing is letting you go — I mean I want to hang on to you, but I can't."

I knew she'd understand.

"Oh, death! I used to dread it; but, now, I really do look forward to that doorway opening — that drawbridge lowering to let me step into the wonderland of praise ahead — and to see you, Nancy. But most of all, to see our Lord — I've never seen Him, as you have, you know.

"I remember how you used to look forward to seeing Him. I know by now you're accustomed to your new life and home.

I know you want me there, too — and your family and friends. But I know you love it there in the meantime.

"But until then, I must live out my life here. We, who are left, must let life be as good as possible, and as you and I learned, that means trusting our Lord all the time.

"I know my life ahead won't be easy. I'll miss you painfully at certain times. You continue to be the most marvelous person I've ever known. But our Lord's Spirit will always be with me.

"To remind me of how good it was for you the moment you crossed that bridge last November, I'm going to imprint one of our favorite passages on the stone above the body you've left behind.

" 'For to me to live *is* Christ, and to die *is* gain.'

"Even though you were very young and beautiful in life, it was still better for you to go to your new home — even better than the apartment that was waiting for us.

"I'll never forget you, Nancy, but I must somehow release you. Hanging on would destroy me and those around me. So — Nancy — good-bye."

I knew she would understand.

I gazed through the window into the darkness outside. Day-break would soon appear, and spring was just a few weeks away.